National 4 & 5

Geography

Human Environments

Calvin Clarke
Susie Clarke

HODDER GIBSON
AN HACHETTE UK COMPANY

The Publishers would like to thank the following for permission to reproduce copyright material:

Photo credits

Chapter opener image on pp.1, 6, 11, 15, 19 and 23 © Daumiu – Fotolia; p.9 (top left) © International Development Issues / Alamy, (top right) © Per-Anders Pettersson/Getty Images, (centre left) © jean claude braun – Fotolia, (centre right) © Moreno Soppelsa – Fotolia, (bottom left) © Pixeltheater – Fotolia, (bottom right) © Greatstock Photographic Library / Alamy; p.10 (top left) © Daumiu – Fotolia, (top right) © Living Legend – Fotolia; Chapter opener image on pp.28, 32, 37 and 42 © Shaen Adey; Gallo Images/Corbis; p.29 (top left) © Ken Hurst – Fotolia, (top right) © Shaen Adey; Gallo Images/Corbis; p.41 (top left) © urosr – Fotolia, (top right) © pablo h. caridad – Fotolia, (centre left) © JAC – Fotolia, (centre right) © nexusseven – Fotolia, (bottom left) © Brian Nolan – Fotolia, (bottom right) © Brad Hunter-Pool/Getty Images; Chapter opener image on pp.46, 50, 56, 60, 64, 68, 72 and 76 © Gordon Thomson; p.50 © Kenny Williamson Glasgow / Alamy; p.51 © c – Fotolia; p.52 © Spaces Images / Alamy; p.53 © Mario Lalich/Photodisc/Getty Images; p.57 © Chris McNulty / Alamy; p.58 © Chris Ware/Keystone Features/Getty Images; p.65 (top left) © Monty Fresco/Topical Press Agency/Getty Images, (top right) © Hulton Archive/Getty Images; p.66 (top) © Gordon Thomson, (bottom) © Crown copyright 2013. All rights reserved. Ordnance Survey licence number 100047450.; p.69 (bottom) © Crown copyright 2013. All rights reserved. Ordnance Survey licence number 100047450.; p.70 © Tony Clerkson / Alamy; p.73 © PR by Loop; p.77 © picsfive – Fotolia; Chapter opener images on pp.81, 87, 92 and 97 © CHI-Photo/Vishwanathan / Rex Features; p.82 © Tim Graham / Alamy; p.83 © CHI-Photo/Vishwanathan / Rex Features; p.88 © JTB MEDIA CREATION, Inc. / Alamy; p.89 © Haytham Pictures / Alamy; p.93 (top) Imagery ©2013 Cnes/Spot Image, DigitalGlobe, Map data ©2013 Google, (bottom) © Joerg Boethling/Still Pictures/ Robert Harding; p.97 © Bethany Clarke/Getty Images; p.99 © David A. Smith, Affordable Housing Institute; Chapter opener image for pp.102, 108 and 113 © Tom Bean / Alamy; p.103 (top) © Don Johnston / Alamy, (bottom) © Paul usna / Alamy; p.108 © Tom Bean / Alamy; p.113 © Wim Wiskerke / Alamy; p.114 © EggImages / Alamy; Chapter opener image for pp.119, 123 and 128 © Ladi Kirn / Alamy; p.125 (top left) © Ladi Kirn / Alamy, (top right) © SAM PANTHAKY/AFP/Getty Images, (bottom left) © NARINDER NANU/AFP/Getty Images, (bottom right) © Joerg Boethling / Alamy.

Acknowledgements

Ordnance Survey maps on pages 66 and 69 are reproduced by permission of Ordnance Survey on behalf of HMSO. © Crown copyright 2013. All rights reserved. Ordnance Survey licence number 100047450.

The text extract on page iv of the Introduction has been quoted from pages 6–7 of the National 5 Geography Course Specification, and has been reproduced with the permission of the Scottish Qualifications Authority.

Every effort has been made to trace all copyright holders, but if any have been inadvertently overlooked the Publishers will be pleased to make the necessary arrangements at the first opportunity.

Although every effort has been made to ensure that website addresses are correct at time of going to press, Hodder Gibson cannot be held responsible for the content of any website mentioned in this book. It is sometimes possible to find a relocated web page by typing in the address of the home page for a website in the URL window of your browser.

Hachette UK's policy is to use papers that are natural, renewable and recyclable products and made from wood grown in sustainable forests. The logging and manufacturing processes are expected to conform to the environmental regulations of the country of origin.

Orders: please contact Bookpoint Ltd, 130 Park Drive, Abingdon, Oxon OX14 4SE. Telephone: (44) 01235 827720. Fax: (44) 01235 400454. Lines are open 9.00–5.00, Monday to Saturday, with a 24-hour message answering service. Visit our website at www.hoddereducation.co.uk. Hodder Gibson can be contacted direct on: Tel: 0141 848 1609; Fax: 0141 889 6315; email: hoddergibson@hodder.co.uk

© Calvin Clarke and Susan Clarke 2013

First published in 2013 by
Hodder Gibson, an imprint of Hodder Education,
An Hachette UK Company
2a Christie Street
Paisley PA1 1NB

Impression number   5 4 3 2 1

Year   2017 2016 2015 2014 2013

ISBN: 978 1 4441 8745 8

Cover photo © xett – Fotolia
Illustrations by Emma Golley at Redmoor Design and Integra Software Services Pvt. Ltd., Pondicherry, India
Typeset in 11 on 12 pt Stempel Schneidler Std Light by Integra Software Services Pvt. Ltd., Pondicherry, India
Printed in Italy
A catalogue record for this title is available from the British Library

Contents

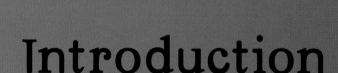

Introduction

This book has been written to cover Unit 2 of the Scottish Qualification Authority's National 4 and National 5 Geography courses.

Unit 2: Human Environments

In this Unit, learners will develop geographical skills and techniques in the context of human environments. The Unit is built around a comparison of developed and developing countries, with the focus on case studies. Key topics include the following.

In the context of developed and developing countries:

■ social and economic indicators
■ physical and human factors influencing global population distribution
■ factors affecting birth and death rates.

In the context of urban areas:

■ characteristics of land use zones in cities in the developed world
■ recent developments in the CBD, inner city and rural/urban fringe in developed world cities
■ recent developments which deal with issues in shanty towns in developing world cities.

In the context of rural areas:

■ changes in the rural landscape in developed countries, related to modern developments in farming, such as diversification, impact of new technology, organic farming, GM, current government policy
■ changes in the rural landscape in developing countries related to modern developments in farming, such as GM, impact of new technology, biofuels.

Each chapter contains N4-level and N5-level questions and Activities. They are designed to develop a knowledge and understanding of human environments but also to develop a range of skills. These include a range of research skills in Outcome 1 but also skills such as literacy, numeracy, enterprise, citizenship and thinking. The N5 questions are mostly similar in style to examination questions; the Activities test the same concepts but encourage active learning and the development of a wider range of skills.

Answers to questions at N4 and N5 are differentiated chiefly according to the amount of detail given. The Activities are differentiated by student response.

Each chapter in the book begins by stating the learning intentions. At the end of the chapter students are asked to self-assess their understanding of these learning intentions using the traffic light system. A photocopiable checklist for all the learning intentions is found at the back of this book for students to use. This 'I can do' self-assessment approach is explained to students on the following page.

'I can do'

Each chapter in this book has a box at the beginning outlining what you will be learning and what you should be able to do after you have completed the N4/N5 questions and Activities. For example:

It is very important that you feel confident about these as you will be assessed on them.

After you have completed each chapter, you will be asked to fill out the 'I can do' boxes for that chapter. These can be found at the back of the book on pages 132–136.

The 'I can do' checklist outlines all of the learning intentions for every chapter within this book. You need to fill it out based on how well you understood the information in the chapter. It is a 'traffic light' system:

This chapter looks at urban and rural populations.

By the end of this chapter you should be able to:

✓ describe the differences in urban and rural populations in developing and developed countries
✓ give reasons for these differences
✓ describe megacities and give examples.

Now complete the 'I can do' boxes for this chapter.

● **RED** means that you DO NOT FEEL THAT YOU UNDERSTAND THIS AND DON'T THINK YOU CAN DO THIS NOW.

◑ **YELLOW** means that you THINK YOU CAN DO MOST OF IT BUT YOU STILL HAVE SOME PROBLEMS.

○ **GREEN** means that you FULLY UNDERSTAND THIS AND YOU CAN DO IT WITHOUT ANY DIFFICULTY.

On the 'I can do' checklist, there is also a space for comments. It is worthwhile taking a few minutes to write a few comments about the chapter, as they will prove very helpful when you start revising. See the example below.

	Red	Yellow	Green	Comment
Chapter 1 World population distribution				
Give examples of countries with a high population density			✓	I can give several examples of countries with a high population density.
Give examples of countries with a low population density			✓	I can give several examples of countries with a low population density.
Describe some of the reasons for the world's population distribution		✓		I can describe some of the reasons for the world's population distribution, but I think there may be more.

Chapter 1

This chapter looks at world population distribution.

World population distribution

By the end of this chapter, you should be able to:

✓ give examples of countries with a high population density
✓ give examples of countries with a low population density
✓ describe some of the reasons for the world's population distribution.

On 31 October 2011 the world population reached 7 billion. Since then, it has been increasing at the rate of 70 million people per year. Eighty-five per cent of all the people in the world live in developing countries (sometimes known as economically less developed countries or ELDCs) and 15 per cent live in developed countries (sometimes known as economically more developed countries or EMDCs). The land area of the world covers 150 million square kilometres (km²). This means there are, on average, over 46 people per km².

Figure 1.1 is a dot map showing the distribution of people around the world. It is clear from this map that people are not distributed evenly around the world. There are both crowded and empty areas, and there are several factors that help to explain why this is so.

1 Climate

People prefer to live where there is rain throughout the year and no extremes of temperature (e.g. north-west Europe). In some areas, the climate limits the number of people who can live there. **Few people live where the climate is very cold** (e.g. northern Russia). The living conditions are unpleasant and expensive. The growing season is too short for crops to grow, so all food has to be imported. It is difficult

1

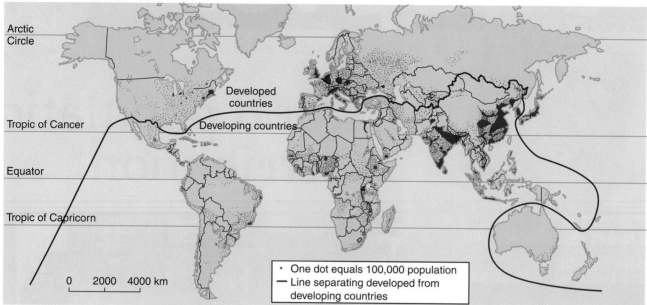

Figure 1.1
World population distribution

to build on ground that is frozen in winter but very muddy in summer. Transport by road, rail and water is hazardous in winter and the remoteness of these regions means few industries set up here. This means that unemployment is high. Also, **few people live where there is little rain** (e.g. the middle of Australia). Again, the conditions are unpleasant and it is difficult to grow crops. The soil is often thin and poor because it is easily eroded by the wind.

2 Soil

Some river valleys are very crowded (e.g. Nile Valley, Ganges Valley). The soil here is fertile alluvium, so it is possible to grow a lot of food in a small area. This means that farms are small. The valley is also flat and the river provides people with a reliable all-year water supply. **Areas with poor soils are sparsely populated**, as the farms need to be very large (e.g. the Amazon Basin).

3 Relief

People prefer to live in flat, lowland areas. Most **mountain ranges in the world are areas of low population density** (e.g. the Himalayas). This is partly because they are cold and their soils are thin. It is also because the slopes are steep, which makes it difficult to build houses, roads and railways, which in turn makes them unattractive for industry.

4 Resources

Where the environment provides useful resources, the population density is higher. Large deposits of minerals, especially coal, have attracted people because of the many employment opportunities (e.g. north-east USA). Other natural resources include attractive scenery, which encourages tourists so people go to work or even retire there (e.g. California).

5 Communications

Areas where there are many roads, railways, airports and ports are more crowded (e.g. north-west Europe). These areas attract industry, which gives many employment opportunities. On the other hand, remote areas deter people (e.g. northern Canada).

6 Technological development

Countries with a lot of natural resources are not crowded if they do not have the money and skills to exploit their resources (e.g. Democratic Republic of the Congo). **Countries with advanced technologies and well-educated people can support higher population densities** (e.g. Japan).

7 Economic activities

Regions where the main activity is industry or services have high population densities (e.g. south-east Australia). Large numbers of people can be employed in a small area. Conversely, **it takes a large area of land to support people who are farming**, especially if the farms are large (e.g. Great Plains, USA).

National 4

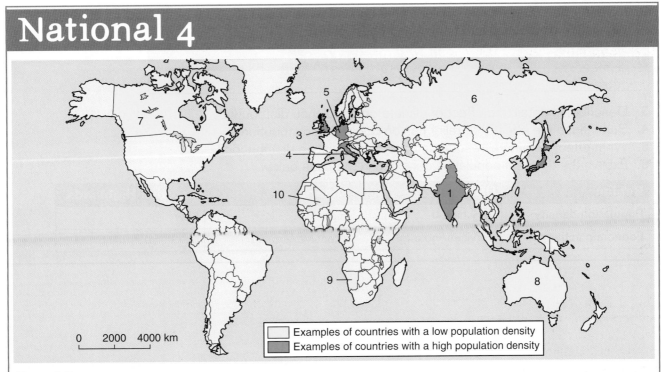

Figure 1.2
Areas of high and low population density in the world

1. Look at Figure 1.2.
   Countries 1–5 have a high population density. Using an atlas, name countries 1–5.
2. Countries 6–10 have a low population density. Name these countries.
3. Look at Figure 1.1.
   (a) Where in the world are the main areas of high population density?
   (b) Where in the world are the main areas of low population density?

National 4 continued...

4. Name (a) two physical and (b) two human factors that affect population distribution.
5. Explain why cold regions attract few people to live.
6. In what ways does relief affect population density?
7. Why are coalfields usually densely populated?
8. Why should countries with low technological development be less crowded?
9. Explain the different population densities in the table below.

Region	USA	Nigeria	Scottish Highlands
Population density	Very high	High	Low
Economic activity	Services/industry	Intensive farming	Extensive farming

National 5

1. Look at Figures 1.1 and 1.2.
   (a) Describe, using examples, the distribution of countries with a high population density.
   (b) Describe, using examples, the distribution of countries with a low population density.
2. In your jotter, draw a table similar to the one below, and classify each of the factors affecting population distribution into human and physical factors.

Human factors	Physical factors

3. Describe, in detail, the effect of climate on population distribution.
4. Summarise the effect that relief has on population distribution.
5. What effect do natural resources have on population distribution?
6. Explain the different population densities in the table below.

Region	USA	Nigeria	Scottish Highlands
Population density	Very high	High	Low
Economic activity	Services/industry	Intensive farming	Extensive farming

Activities

Activity A

Look at the table below showing different countries and their population, area and density.

Country	Population	Area (km²)	Density (number of people per km²)
United Kingdom	62,000,000	250,000	255
Greenland	56,000	2,000,000	0.026
Switzerland	8,000,000	41,000	188
USA	315,000,000	8,000,000	32
New Zealand	4,000,000	300,000	16
Japan	128,000,000	400,000	337

1. Rank each of the countries from highest to lowest by **population**.
2. Rank each country from highest to lowest by **size**.
3. Rank each country from highest to lowest by **density**.

Activity B

Draw a bar graph to show (a) the population and (b) the population density of the six countries in the table.

Now complete the 'I can do' boxes for this chapter.

Chapter 2

Urban and rural population

This chapter looks at urban and rural populations.

By the end of this chapter, you should be able to:

✓ describe the differences in urban and rural populations in developed and developing countries
✓ give reasons for these differences
✓ describe megacities and give examples.

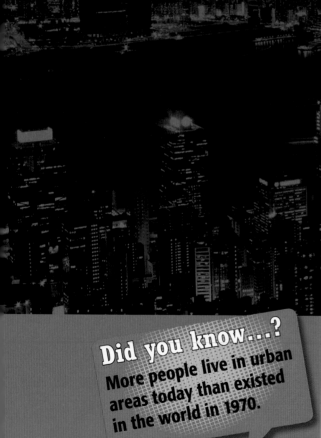

Did you know…?
More people live in urban areas today than existed in the world in 1970.

	Urban population	Rural population
World	51%	49%
Developed	78%	22%
Developing	43%	57%

Figure 2.1
Urban and rural populations in 2011

Figure 2.1 shows that more than half of the world's people live in towns and cities, but **the urban population is higher in more developed countries than in less developed countries**. In developing countries many more people make a living from farming and so live in the countryside. In developed countries, for example USA, most jobs are in offices, services and factories, which are mostly found in towns and cities.

	Urban population	Rural population
World	29%	71%
Developed	54%	46%
Developing	17%	83%

Figure 2.2
Urban and rural populations in 1950

By comparing Figures 2.1 and 2.2 we can see that **the proportion of people living in cities has increased a lot since 1950.** This trend is called **urbanisation.** All over the world cities are becoming more popular, but **in developing countries the percentage of people living in cities is rising faster than in developed countries.**

In developing countries, people are moving to cities because of **push factors** from the countryside. Because the population is rising, there is not enough land for everyone to farm. In addition, there is the ever-present problem of crop failure and, even, natural disasters. Services are much poorer in the countryside, with fewer medical facilities and schools, as well as fewer basic amenities such as sewage disposal, electricity and water. On the other hand, cities provide more and better services, including shops and entertainments. Most offices and factories are in cities, so there are also more job opportunities. Although cities have many problems, this is not slowing down the number of people who are attracted to live there.

In developed countries, the push factors from the countryside are similar. People are moving away because there are fewer jobs in farming and they are poorly paid. The countryside also lacks shops and entertainments, as well as being further from train stations, ports and airports. Cities have better-paid jobs in services and high-tech industries, and they have a greater variety of housing. They also have problems, such as high crime rates, high pollution levels and traffic congestion. These problems have reduced the number of people moving to cities and, in some cases, there are now more people leaving them than moving in.

Did you know....?
Four million km² of the Earth's surface has been paved to accommodate the growing urban population.

Megacities

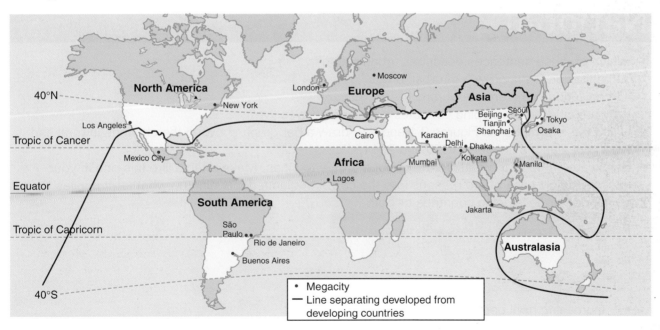

Figure 2.3
World distribution of megacities

Figure 2.3 shows the distribution of the world's biggest cities. Each city has over 10 million people living there and is called a megacity. As would be expected, the pattern is similar to the global distribution of people, shown in Figure 1.1 in Chapter 1. Although developed countries have a higher rate of urbanisation, **it is the developing countries in which most of the megacities are found** (see Figure 2.4). In developed countries, people have a choice of many cities to which they can move. In developing countries, there are usually just one or two cities that attract most of the people from the entire country.

City	Developed or developing	Population (millions)	Annual growth rate (%)
Tokyo	Developed	36.0	0.6
Shanghai	Developed	25.3	2.2
Mexico City	Developing	23.2	2.0
Mumbai	Developing	20.8	2.9
São Paulo	Developing	21.1	1.4
New York	Developed	21.5	0.3
Lagos	Developing	12.7	3.2
Los Angeles	Developed	17.6	1.1
Kolkata	Developing	15.7	2.0
Buenos Aires	Developing	14.3	1.0

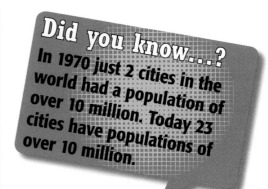

Did you know....?
In 1970 just 2 cities in the world had a population of over 10 million. Today 23 cities have populations of over 10 million.

Figure 2.4
The world's biggest cities

National 4

1. Which of these sentences describes urbanisation?
   'Urbanisation is the growth of urban areas.'
   'Urbanisation is the growth of rural areas.'
2. Why are cities in developing countries popular places to live?
3. Using the information in Figures 2.1 and 2.2, draw a bar graph showing the changes in rural and urban populations between 1950 and 2011.
4. Below are some of the reasons why people move to cities. Make a table like this one in your jotter, and sort each of the reasons into the correct column depending on whether it applies to developed or developing countries or both.

Developed countries	Developing countries

   - Increasing rural population
   - Not enough farmland
   - Crop failure
   - Poorer services in the countryside
   - Fewer hospitals and schools in the countryside
   - Better electricity and water supply in cities
   - Few rural shops
5. Using Figure 2.3, describe where most of the megacities in the world are found, giving examples.
6. Using Figure 2.4, compare the increase in the populations of megacities in developing and developed countries since 1950.

National 5

1. What is meant by *urbanisation*?
2. Using the information in Figures 2.1 and 2.2, draw a bar graph showing the changes in rural and urban populations between 1950 and 2011.
3. Using Figures 2.1 and 2.2, compare the increase since 1950 of people living in cities in developing and developed countries.
4. Explain why cities in developing countries are popular places in which to live.
5. Do people in developed countries move to cities for the same reasons as people in developing countries? Give reasons for your answer.
6. Use Figure 2.3 to describe the global distribution of megacities.
7. Use Figure 2.4 to compare the increase since 1950 of the populations of megacities in developing and developed countries.

Activities

Activity A

Below are pictures showing the 'push' and 'pull' reasons why people move from the countryside to the cities in developing countries. Study each picture carefully.

1. Write down what you think each picture is showing.
2. Describe the effect of what you have noted on people's decisions to move to a city.

A

B

C

D

E

F

Activities continued...

G

H

Activity B

Below is a letter from a student explaining what it is like living in the countryside in India. You should pretend to be a student living in Mumbai (India's biggest city): write a letter back to him explaining what life is like in the city. You should focus on the same things as he does.

Hello, my name is Abdul and I'm 15 years old. I live in the countryside about 50 km outside of Mumbai. I live with my mum, dad, three sisters and two brothers. We have a small patch of land that we grow crops on. We also have a few animals – a couple of cows and some chickens. The food that we grow is what we have to live on, so if our crops don't grow very well, we don't have much to eat. Recently, our crops haven't grown well at all because it hasn't rained much. To get water my three sisters and my mum have to walk about 4 km to the nearest river. The water isn't very clean and it doesn't taste very nice, but you get used to it. Me and my two brothers go to school but my sisters aren't allowed to because they're needed to help at home. There are 50 pupils in my class and only one teacher. We learn things like adding and subtracting and spelling but my favourite is learning about different countries in the world. All our lessons are outside and we only go to school in the morning, so in the afternoon my youngest brother goes back to the farm to help while me and my other brother go to work. We both work as brick-makers. It's a difficult job and we don't get paid very much for it, but every little helps. It means we can buy extra food for the family.

I've heard people talk about 'weekends' and what they do, but every day is the same for us. We don't have school on a Saturday or Sunday but my brother and me both work on Saturdays, and on Sundays we help out on the farm. Sometimes one of the families nearby will have a celebration and we'll go to see them – that's fun.

Life in the countryside is very difficult and I often wonder what it would be like to live in a big city like Mumbai. Maybe you could tell me all about it and how your life is different from mine. Maybe one day I'll be able to move to the city.

Now complete the 'I can do' boxes for this chapter.

Chapter 3

This chapter looks at how and why populations change.

Population change

By the end of this chapter, you should be able to:

✓ describe what is meant by birth rate, death rate and natural increase

✓ outline the difference in birth rates and death rates between developing and developed countries

✓ give reasons for these differences.

Figure 3.1 shows the changes in the world's population since the year 1750. It shows that **the number of people in the world is increasing**. It also shows that **this number is increasing at an faster rate**. Each year the number of extra people on the planet is greater than in the previous year. Figure 3.1 is a composite line graph. As well as showing the world's population change, it also shows the population change in the more developed and less developed world. The number of people in developed countries has grown from nearly 200 million in 1750 to 1200 million in 2012. The population grew very quickly between 1875 and 1960. The number of people in developing countries has grown from over 500 million in 1750 to 6000 million in 2012. This population grew more slowly than in developed countries until 1925. Since then, it has grown at a very rapid rate.

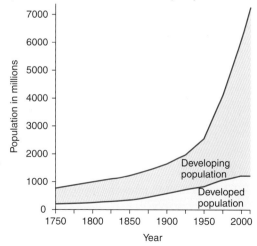

Figure 3.1
Population growth of developed and developing countries, 1750–2012

Birth rates and death rates

The number of people in the world is increasing because there are more people being born than there are people dying. The number of people being born is called the birth rate (BR) and is defined as the number of births per 1000 people (‰) in a year.

The number of people dying is called the death rate (DR) and is defined as the number of deaths per 1000 people (‰) in a year. **The difference between the birth rate and the death rate is called the natural increase (NI).**

The average birth rate throughout the world now is 20‰ and the average death rate is 8‰. This gives a natural increase of population in the world of $20 - 8 = 12‰$. Birth rates and death rates are higher in developing countries than in developed countries. This is shown in Figures 3.2 and 3.3.

Factors affecting births

Developing countries have more births – a higher birth rate. This is due to a number of factors:

- Children can take care of their parents in their old age.
- Children can help their families on farms or by earning money.
- Infant mortality (death) rates are high in developing countries.
- There is a lack of contraception and family planning.
- In some cultures, large families have a high status.

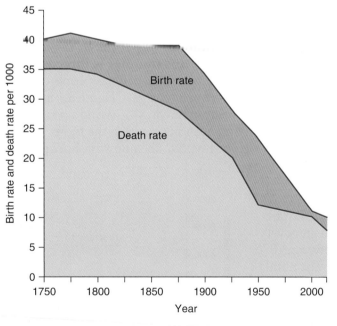

Figure 3.2
Changes in birth rates and death rates in developed countries, 1750–2012

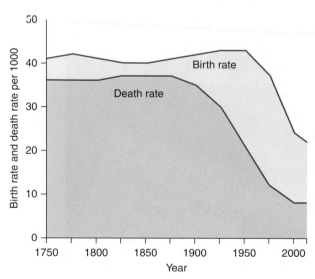

Figure 3.3
Changes in birth rates and death rates in developing countries, 1750–2012

Developed countries have fewer births – a lower birth rate – because:

- More women work and have a career.
- People get married later.
- Contraception and family planning are widely available.
- Children are very expensive to raise.

Factors affecting death rates

Developing countries have higher death rates because:

- There is a lack of clean water.
- Many people live in poor housing with poor sanitation.
- Many people do not have enough to eat.
- Diseases are more widespread.
- There are fewer medical facilities.

You should note that in developing countries the death rate is 8‰, the same as in developed countries. But people die at a younger age in developing countries, so statistics are distorted by the greater number of old people in developed countries.

Developed countries have low death rates because:

- Safe, clean water is provided.
- Proper sanitation facilities are provided.
- People are generally well fed.
- Advanced medical facilities and advice are available.

National 4

1. Compare the growth in population in developing and developed countries since 1750.
2. What is the connection between birth rate, death rate and population change?
3. (a) Calculate the natural increase for each of the following:

   Country A: Birth rate 35‰   Death rate 21‰

   Country B: Birth rate 15‰   Death rate 13‰

   (b) Which country (A or B) is more likely to be a developing country? Give reasons for your choice.
4. Both birth rates and death rates are high in developing countries. Why is this?
5. Death rates are low in developed countries. What improvements have allowed this to happen?

National 5

1. Compare the growth in population in developing and developed countries since 1750.
2. What is the connection between birth rates, death rates and population change?
3. (a) Calculate the natural increase for each of the following:

   Country A: Birth rate 43‰   Death rate 26‰

   Country B: Birth rate 13‰   Death rate 13‰

   (b) Which country (A or B) is more likely to be a developing country? Give detailed reasons for your choice.
4. Why are birth rates lower in developed than in developing countries?
5. Why do people die at a younger age in developing than in developed countries?

Activities

1 high status	2 later marriage	3 children are expensive
4 disease is widespread	5 lack of clean water	6 poor housing
7 lack of contraception	8 few medical facilities	9 safe, clean water
10 good housing	11 high infant mortality rates	12 poor diets
13 advanced medical facilities	14 children take care of parents in old age	15 improved sanitation

1. Examine carefully each of the groups of words in the table above. Make sure that you understand what these terms mean.
2. Now look at the table below. There are ten rows. The numbers refer to the terms above.
   (a) For each row, decide which of the three terms is the odd one out.
   (b) State why it is the odd one out.
   Group A has been done for you as an example. Remember, it is your explanation that is the most important here.

   > 1 = high status   7 = lack of contraception   3 = children are expensive
   > *All three terms are to do with births but 'children are expensive' is the odd one out because the other two terms are reasons for a high birth rate in developing countries.*

Group			
A	1	7	3
B	14	11	9
C	15	13	12
D	5	4	14
E	11	1	2
F	9	10	3
G	1	4	7
H	8	2	5
I	13	7	10
J	8	14	11

Now complete the 'I can do' boxes for this chapter.

Chapter

> This chapter looks at countries with rapid population growth.

The effects of rapid population growth

By the end of this chapter, you should be able to:

✓ describe birth and death rates in countries with rapidly growing populations

✓ describe the problems associated with countries with a rapid population growth

✓ describe the benefits for countries with a rapid population growth.

Population structure

In many developing countries, birth rates are much higher than death rates and the population is rising rapidly. In these countries the population structure is similar to that shown in Figure 4.1.

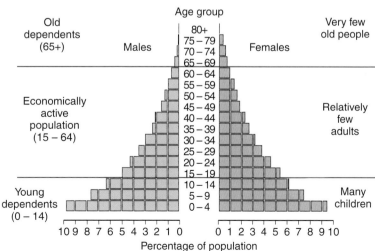

Old dependents (65+)   Males   Females   Very few old people

Economically active population (15 – 64)   Relatively few adults

Young dependents (0 – 14)   Many children

Age group: 80+, 75 – 79, 70 – 74, 65 – 69, 60 – 64, 55 – 59, 50 – 54, 45 – 49, 40 – 44, 35 – 39, 30 – 34, 25 – 29, 20 – 24, 15 – 19, 10 – 14, 5 – 9, 0 – 4

10 9 8 7 6 5 4 3 2 1 0   0 1 2 3 4 5 6 7 8 9 10

Percentage of population

Figure 4.1
Typical population structure of a developing country

There are many children because the birth rate is high. Often, as much as one-half of the population is under 15 years of age. There are fewer people of working age (15–60 years) because, until recently, the death rate was high and many children did not survive until adulthood. For the same reason, there are very few old people.

This population structure brings problems. **Less than half the population is of working age, and they have to provide for the rest of the people.** Because there are so many births, **the country needs to spend a lot of money on hospitals, doctors and nurses.** And, once the children have reached school age, there is the **expense of providing schools and teachers**.

Advantages of rapid growth

Some developing countries are pleased that their populations are rising rapidly. They become more powerful and less vulnerable to attack, as **they have a large number of people available for the armed forces**. There is **an increasing number of workers**, which should increase production on farms and in factories and offices. More workers means that **wage rates are lower** which, in turn, attracts international companies wanting to reduce their labour costs.

Disadvantages of rapid growth

However, a rapidly rising population also brings many problems. In rural areas, **the farms are becoming smaller** and farmers have to farm the land more intensively in order to grow enough food. This only makes the soil poorer. **More and more trees are being cut down** to create more farmland or to provide fuel and building material. This, in turn, allows the soil to be blown away or washed away. **The land becomes even more infertile, fewer crops grow, the people become poor and hungry and many move to cities.**

In urban areas, the population is increasing even more rapidly because of immigrants from the countryside. The authorities cannot build enough houses for everyone, so **people build their own shacks which lack even basic amenities**, such as toilets and a water supply. There are not enough jobs for everyone, so **unemployment is high** and **crime rates rise. Traffic congestion worsens.** Services cannot cope with the extra people, so **schools and hospitals are overcrowded**, and not everyone has access to them.

Controlling rapid growth

Most developing countries wish to slow down their population growth. Many measures are used and some of these are shown in Figure 4.2.

- Laws limiting family size, e.g. the one-child policy in China since 1979
- More information given out on how to reduce births, e.g. more family planning clinics
- Greater education of females, as evidence suggest that regions in which female education is higher are also areas where birth rates are lower
- More opportunities for abortion and sterilisation
- Incentives given to limit family size, e.g. free health care and preferential housing

Figure 4.2
Some measures to reduce birth rates

At the same time, **countries are trying hard to improve farming** so that they can continue to feed everyone. High-yielding crops are used, more fertilisers and pesticides are being applied, and more land is being reclaimed and irrigated.

National 4

1. Describe birth rates and death rates in countries with a rapidly growing population.
2. Describe the problems faced by a country with many young people and few adults.
3. Make a list of the advantages of a rapidly growing population.
4. Explain why a rapidly growing population leads to (a) poor soils and (b) emigration from the countryside to cities.
5. Describe three problems that cities in developing countries face because of a rapidly growing population.
6. Look at Figure 4.2. Which two measures of reducing birth rates do you think will be most effective? Give reasons for your answer.

National 5

1. Describe the population structure of a country with a rapidly growing population.
2. What problems does this population structure bring?
3. Describe and explain the benefits brought by a rapidly growing population.
4. Explain why a rapidly growing population leads to (a) poor soils and (b) emigration from the countryside to cities.
5. Describe four problems that cities in developing countries face because of a rapidly growing population.
6. Look at Figure 4.2. Which three measures of reducing birth rates do you think will be most effective? Give reasons for your answer.

Activities

The table below shows the number of males and females in a small country.

Draw a population pyramid (similar to the one in Figure 4.1) to show this information. Use a large copy of Figure 4.3 as a template for your pyramid.

Colour the bars for males in one colour and the bars for females in another colour.

Age group	Males (thousands)	Females (thousands)
80+	20	40
70–79	60	80
60–69	120	110
50–59	140	140
40–49	180	220
30–39	170	280
20–29	270	310
10–19	380	350
0–9	350	330

Activities continued...

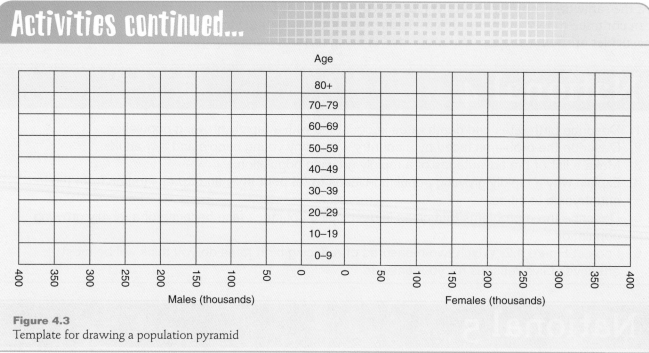

Figure 4.3
Template for drawing a population pyramid

Now complete the 'I can do' boxes for this chapter.

Chapter 5

The effects of slow population growth

This chapter looks at countries with slowly growing populations.

By the end of this chapter, you should be able to:

✓ describe birth and death rates in countries with slowly growing populations
✓ describe the problems for countries with slowly growing populations
✓ describe the benefits for countries with slowly growing populations.

In most developed countries the birth rates and death rates are low and their **populations are rising only slowly, if at all**. Their population structures are similar to the one shown in Figure 5.1.

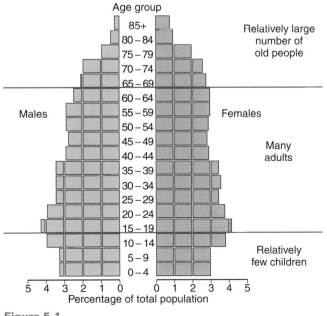

Figure 5.1
Typical population structure of a developed country

There are few children in the population because the birth rate is so low. There are many adults because, in the past, the birth rate was higher and many of the children born at that time have survived into adulthood. There are also many old people because the death rate is so low and most people live to an old age.

This structure has advantages over the one for a typical developing country, shown in Figure 4.1 in the previous chapter. There are more people of working age and **less money needs to be spent on education** because there are far fewer children. But the structure is not ideal, as shown by the data for the UK in Figure 5.2.

Age group	1950 (%)	2012 (%)
0–14 years	22	18
15–64 years	67	63
65 years and over	11	19

Figure 5.2
Population structure of the UK, 1950 and 2012

The number of old people in the population is increasing rapidly (the so-called 'greying of the population'). More money is, therefore, needed to pay for pensions. **More care services** (e.g. day care, meals on wheels) **are required**, as are **sheltered houses** and **old people's homes**. Old people use **health services** more, so the cost of health care rises. These costs are paid for by taxes, but **there are now fewer people of working age who pay tax**. This also means there is a decreasing number of people for the armed forces, and fewer potential parents.

Solutions

Many developed countries are concerned about their slow population growth. Some of the measures they have adopted to solve their problems are given in Figure 5.3.

In France, mothers with three children can take a year off work – and receive up to 900 euros a month from the government to stay at home. Families get cheaper public transport and holiday vouchers. All mothers receive about 200 euros a month until their child is 3 years old.

- More paternity leave, to encourage parents to have more children, e.g. in the UK fathers have two weeks of paid leave
- More maternity benefits such as those provided in France
- Raise retirement age, to increase the number of taxpayers and reduce pensions, e.g. in the UK retirement age for women was raised to 65 in 2010
- Encourage more women to work, which increases the workforce and the number of taxpayers, e.g. more retraining schemes, provision of crèches in the workplace
- Allow in more immigrants, to increase the number of taxpayers and workers
- Encourage people to take out private pension schemes, to reduce the cost of providing public pensions

Figure 5.3
Policies for slowly growing populations

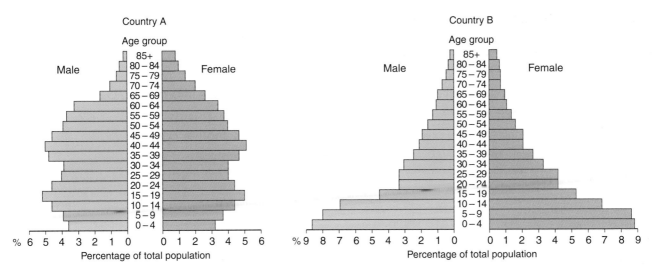

Figure 5.4
The population structures for two countries

National 4

Using the information in Figure 5.4:

1. Which country, A or B, has (a) the higher birth rate and (b) the higher death rate?
2. Which country, A or B, is showing the typical population structure for a developing country?
3. What is meant by the phrase 'the greying of the population'?
4. List the problems associated with a slowly growing population.
5. Describe ways in which developed countries can increase their workforce.
6. Choose two of the policies for slowly growing populations (Figure 5.3). State whether you think they are good ideas, and why.

National 5

Using the information in Figure 5.4:

1. Compare the population structures for countries A and B.
2. In developed countries populations are rising very slowly. Explain why their governments face increased costs in providing for their population.
3. What problems are created when the number of people of working age begins to fall?
4. Describe the ways in which developed countries can increase their workforce.
5. Choose two of the policies for slowly growing populations (Figure 5.3). State whether you think they are good ideas. Explain fully why.

Activities

The table below shows the number of males and females in a small country.

Draw a population pyramid (similar to the one in Figure 5.1) to show this information. Use a large copy of Figure 4.3 on page 18 as a template for your pyramid.

Colour the bars for males in one colour and the bars for females in another colour.

Age group	Males (thousands)	Females (thousands)
80+	70	95
70–79	185	190
60–69	220	215
50–59	265	270
40–49	300	300
30–39	255	260
20–29	230	250
10–19	150	150
0–9	160	155

Now complete the 'I can do' boxes for this chapter.

Chapter 6

This chapter looks at the Demographic Transition Model.

The Demographic Transition Model

By the end of this chapter, you should be able to:

✓ describe how the population changes at each stage of the Demographic Transition Model
✓ explain why birth rates and death rates change at each stage
✓ give examples of countries that fit into each stage.

The Demographic Transition Model (DTM) shows the changes in birth rates and death rates of a typical country over time. The DTM has four main stages, and countries move from one stage to the next over time. The least developed countries might still be in Stages 1 and 2, while the most developed countries are in Stage 4. There is now thought to be a Stage 5 too.

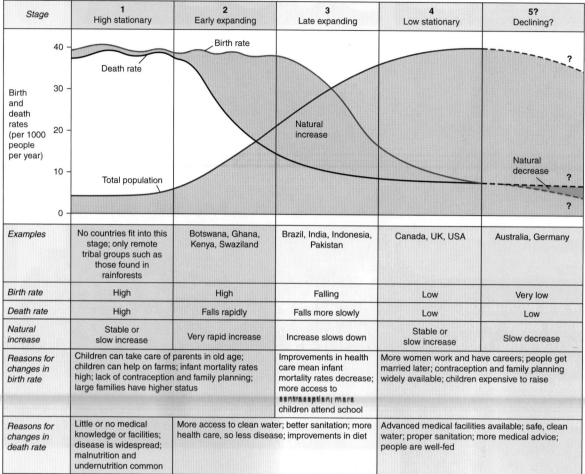

Stage	1 High stationary	2 Early expanding	3 Late expanding	4 Low stationary	5? Declining?
Examples	No countries fit into this stage; only remote tribal groups such as those found in rainforests	Botswana, Ghana, Kenya, Swaziland	Brazil, India, Indonesia, Pakistan	Canada, UK, USA	Australia, Germany
Birth rate	High	High	Falling	Low	Very low
Death rate	High	Falls rapidly	Falls more slowly	Low	Low
Natural increase	Stable or slow increase	Very rapid increase	Increase slows down	Stable or slow increase	Slow decrease
Reasons for changes in birth rate	Children can take care of parents in old age; children can help on farms; infant mortality rates high; lack of contraception and family planning; large families have higher status		Improvements in health care mean infant mortality rates decrease; more access to contraception; more children attend school	More women work and have careers; people get married later; contraception and family planning widely available; children expensive to raise	
Reasons for changes in death rate	Little or no medical knowledge or facilities; disease is widespread; malnutrition and undernutrition common	More access to clean water; better sanitation; more health care, so less disease; improvements in diet		Advanced medical facilities available; safe, clean water; proper sanitation; more medical advice; people are well-fed	

Figure 6.1
The Demographic Transition Model

Stage 1 – A high stationary population

- Both birth rates and death rates are very high.
- Total population is very low.
- Natural increase is low.

There are very few countries in Stage 1 today – possibly only remote groups in the rainforest.
The UK was in Stage 1 before 1760.

Stage 2 – An early expanding population

- Birth rates are still high.
- Death rates are falling.
- Total population is increasing.
- Natural increase is high.

Some of the poorest developing countries are still in Stage 2, such as Malawi and Bangladesh.
The UK was in Stage 2 between 1760 and 1900.

Stage 3 – A late expanding population

- Birth rates are falling.
- Death rates are also continuing to fall.
- Total population is increasing.
- Natural increase is quite high.

Most developing countries are in Stage 3, such as Brazil.
The UK was in Stage 3 between 1900 and 1950.

Stage 4 – A low stationary population

- Both birth rates and death rates are low.
- Total population is steady.
- Natural increase is very low.

Most developed countries are in Stage 4, such as the UK and USA.
The UK has been in Stage 4 since the 1950s.

Stage 5 – A declining population

- Death rates remain low.
- Birth rates are low and decreasing.
- Total population is decreasing.
- Natural increase is negative.

Some developed countries are now in Stage 5, such as Australia and Germany.

National 4

1. What does the Demographic Transition Model show?
2. Look at Figure 6.1.
   (a) Describe the changes in birth rates in a typical country over time.
   (b) Describe the changes in death rates in a typical country over time.
   (c) Describe the changes in population in a typical country over time.
3. Explain why a country's population:
   (a) grows slowly during Stage 1
   (b) grows quickly during Stage 2.
4. Which stage of the DTM has:
   (a) high birth rates and decreasing death rates
   (b) birth rates lower than death rates
   (c) low death rates and decreasing birth rates
   (d) birth and death rates both very high
   (e) low birth and death rates?
5. Why are birth rates high in Stage 1?
6. Give reasons for death rates falling in Stage 2.

National 5

1. What is the purpose of the Demographic Transition Model?
2. Look at Figure 6.1.
   (a) Describe the changes in a country's birth rate and death rate over time.
   (b) Explain the changes in natural increase of the population over time.
3. Why are birth rates high in Stage 2?
4. Give reasons for death rates falling in Stage 3.
5. What problems might occur for a country in Stage 5 of the DTM?

Activities

Activity A

Using Figure 6.1 to help you, decide which of the stages (1–5) in the DTM is most likely to experience the following:

(a) plenty of doctors and nurses for the population
(b) a large number of patients per doctor
(c) a sudden improvement in family planning
(d) children with plenty of expensive toys
(e) large-scale immigration, particularly people of working age
(f) few families with grandparents
(g) very few trained doctors
(h) families with lots of children working on farms
(i) a rapid increase in houses being built
(j) young couples going on many holidays each year.

Activity B

Read through the information for the five countries below and decide into which stage of the DTM each country fits.

Country 1

GDP per capita: $619

Birth rate: 35/1000

Death rate: 15/1000

Country 2

GDP per capita: $45,903

Birth rate: 7/1000

Death rate: 9/1000

Country 3

GDP per capita: $443

Birth rate: 40/1000

Death rate: 35/1000

Country 4

GDP per capita: $2781

Birth rate: 22/1000

Death rate: 10/1000

Activities continued...

Country 5

GDP per capita: $ 28,423

Birth rate: 13/1000

Death rate: 8/1000

Activity C

Look at the table below. Some of the boxes are incomplete. Try to complete them, choosing from four options in each case:

(a) Birth rate of Nigeria   60   40   20   10
(b) Death rate of Germany   21   16   11   7
(c) Life expectancy of India   79   72   65   46
(d) Infant mortality in Canada   20   15   10   5
(e) GNP per capita of Italy   41   33   23   11
(f) Contribution of agriculture
     to GDP in Bangladesh   38   34   30   18

Country	GNP ($ per capita)	Birth rate	Death rate	Stage in DTM (1–5)	% contribution of agriculture to GDP	Life expectancy	Infant mortality (per 1000)
Nigeria	1,200		17	2	35	46	96
France	40,000	12	9	4	2	80	3
Germany	40,000	9		5	1	79	3
India	1,400	21	8	3	17		52
Malawi	900	45	13	2	30	52	79
Canada	46,400	11	7	4	2	80	
South Africa	7,300	21	17	3	3	49	54
Italy		9	11	5	2	82	3
Bangladesh	670	20	8	3		64	48

Now complete the 'I can do' boxes for this chapter.

Chapter 7

This chapter looks at how we measure a country's level of development.

Measuring development (1)

By the end of this chapter, you should be able to:

✓ provide a definition for development
✓ give examples of economic indicators of development
✓ describe social indicators of development.

This book studies important geographical issues on a world scale, and none is more important than the huge differences in health and wealth from country to country.

Most countries are trying to improve the conditions in which their people live. **Any improvement that is made in the standard of living of the people is called *development*.**

Some countries are more developed than others. Their people enjoy a high standard of living. These are the developed or economically more developed countries (EMDCs). Those that have not developed as much are called developing or economically less developed countries (ELDCs). Their people have a much lower standard of living.

Measuring development

It is very difficult to work out one person's standard of living. To try and measure precisely the standard of living of all the people in a country is impossible. The best that can be done is to select a few indicators of development and measure these indicators, for example people's average income, life expectancy, education or food intake. Two development indicators are studied here.

Figure 7.1
This large house and expensive car demonstrates a rich lifestyle
and a high standard of living, in economic terms.

Figure 7.2
In this shanty town in Natal in South Africa, conditions are poor
and the standard of living is low.

Economic indicators of development

Economic indicators are commonly used indicators. **They measure the wealth
and level of industrialisation of a country.** Examples include the following:

Gross domestic product (GDP) per person

The **gross domestic product** (GDP) is the value of all the goods produced and
services provided in a country in one year. This is divided by the number of people
living in the country to indicate the wealth of the average person.

Gross national product (GNP) per person

The **gross national product** is similar to the GDP, but it also includes services
earned abroad.

Energy used per person

The amount of energy (coal, oil, gas, etc.) that is used in a country can also indicate
economic development. Countries with a lot of industries producing much wealth
will also use a lot of energy. People with a high standard of living will use a lot of
petrol in their motor cars and lots of electricity in their homes.

People employed in agriculture

A country with a high proportion of its people working in agriculture will have
little industry to produce wealth. In addition, its farms are likely to be small and
unprofitable. So a high percentage of people in agriculture is a good indicator of a
less developed country, and vice versa.

Problems with economic indicators

- Although a country may produce a lot of wealth, it may not be spread out amongst all of its people. A small number may be extremely wealthy while the vast majority remain poor.
- The amount of wealth does not give enough information on people's quality of life, for example how healthy they are, or how well educated.
- The amount of income and wealth does not even show how well-off the people are. This needs to be compared with prices to find out what people can buy with that amount of money.

Social indicators of development

Social indicators show how a country uses its wealth to improve the **quality of life** of its people. Those indicators that measure health include:

- population per doctor
- infant mortality (the number of children who die before they are 1 year old)
- life expectancy.

Those that measure diet include:

- calories per person per day
- protein per person per day.

Those that measure education include:

- percentage of children attending primary school
- adult literacy.

Problems with social indicators

- Social indicators also use averages, so they do not tell us the differences within a country. For example, the average number of calories per person might be 2500 per day, but half of the people might only receive 2000 calories and be severely undernourished, while the other half have 3000 calories and are well fed.
- One indicator on its own does not give enough information on quality of life. Although people may be well fed, we do not know how healthy or how well educated they are.

National 4

1. What is meant by 'development'?
2. Describe two economic indicators of development.
3. Name four social indicators of development.
4. What is the difference between an economic indicator and a social indicator of development?
5. Most indicators give average figures. Describe the problems with using averages.

National 5

1. What is meant by the term 'development'?
2. Choose two economic indicators of development and describe how each shows the development level of a country.
3. What are the differences between economic indicators and social indicators of development?
4. Choose three social indicators of development (one from each category) and describe how each shows the development level of a country.
5. Overall, what are the problems with using only one type of indicator to measure development?

Activities

Activity A

Look at the table below which shows six indicators of development for France and the UK.

Indicator of development	France	UK
Average income ($)	27,789	26,500
Life expectancy (years)	81	80
Population per doctor	324	280
Calories eaten per person per day	3,550	3,400
Number of cars per 1000 people	578	525
Percentage of people working in agriculture	3	2

1. What is the best indicator of the standards of living in France and the UK? Give reasons for your answer.
2. Which country is more developed – Britain or France? Give reasons for your answer.

Activity B

1. Working either on your own or with a partner, read through each of the statements below and decide whether they are more likely to apply to a developed or to a developing country.
   - The country has a high gross national product.
   - Many people work in agriculture.
   - Only small amounts of energy are used per person.
   - Most people in the country are able to read and write.
   - There are many patients per doctor.
   - People consume many calories each day.
   - Many people in the country live to an old age.
   - Many of the babies born survive infancy.
2. Give reasons for each of the decisions you made.

Now complete the 'I can do' boxes for this chapter.

Chapter

8

Measuring development (2)

This chapter looks at combined indicators of development.

By the end of this chapter, you should be able to:

✓ give reasons why combined indicators of development are more reliable than single indicators
✓ describe the Physical Quality of Life Index
✓ describe the Human Development Index.

Comparing social and economic indicators

Generally, countries that score highly on economic indicators also do well according to social indicators. This is because they can use their wealth to provide proper schooling, hospitals, food and decent housing. Countries with little wealth just cannot afford to provide all of these social services for their people.

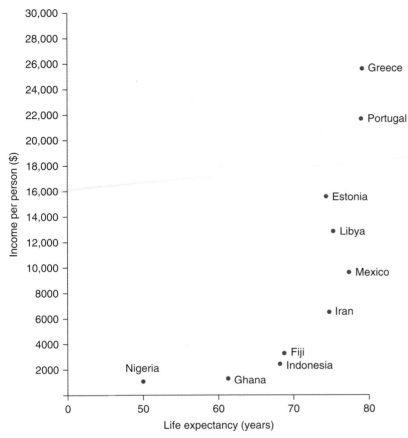

Figure 8.1
Life expectancy and income in selected countries

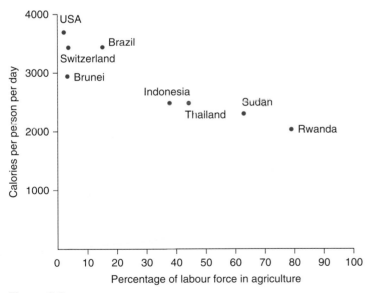

Figure 8.2
Agricultural labour force and calorie intake in selected countries

Some countries, however, appear more developed according to social indicators while others appear more developed according to economic indicators. This is shown in Figures 8.1 and 8.2. For example, Figure 8.1 shows that as a country's income per person increases, so does the life expectancy of its people. But, some exceptions can be spotted. For example, people in Mexico have a higher life expectancy than people in Estonia, but their average income is much lower.

Combined indicators of development

Did you know...?
According to the HDI, the most developed country is Norway and the least developed is the Democratic Republic of Congo.

Indicator of development	China	India
GNP per person ($)	4,940	1,410
Energy used per person (kg)	1,807	566
Life expectancy (years)	72	64
Calories per person per day	2,970	2,300
Adult literacy (%)	92	74

Figure 8.3
Using five indicators of development to compare China and India

Because different indicators give different results, it is more reliable to use several indicators. Often, **a range of social and economic indicators are used**. For example, to compare the development of the two most populous countries in the world, in Figure 8.3 five indicators have been used. According to all of these, China is more developed than India. Alternatively, **a range of indicators can be used to produce a single combined index**. Two examples of such indexes are:

■ Physical Quality of Life Index (PQLI) – this combines life expectancy, infant mortality and adult literacy to produce an index from 0 to 100. The higher the PQLI, the higher the quality of life of the country. A PQLI of over 77 is considered good.
■ Human Development Index (HDI) – this combines life expectancy, adult literacy, GNP/person, cost of living and school enrolment to produce an index from 0 to 1, where an HDI of 0.8 or above is considered developed.

	Highest PQLI	Highest HDI
1	Ireland	Norway
2	Switzerland	Australia
3	Norway	Netherlands
4	Luxembourg	United States
5	Sweden	New Zealand
6	Australia	Canada
7	Iceland	Ireland
8	Italy	Liechtenstein
9	Denmark	Germany
10	Spain	Sweden

Figure 8.4
The world's ten most developed countries

National 4

1. Why do countries that score highly on economic indicators usually also score highly on social indicators?
2. Why is it more reliable to use several indicators?
3. What factors make up the Physical Quality of Life Index (PQLI)?
4. If a country has a PQLI of 86, is it considered more or less developed than a country with a PQLI of 53?
5. How many of the factors that make up the PQLI are (a) social and (b) economic?
6. What factors make up the Human Development Index (HDI)?
7. From the information in Figure 8.4, do you think the PQLI and HDI give similar results?
8. Look at Figure 8.1. What is the life expectancy and income per person in (a) Greece and (b) Nigeria?
9. Look at Figure 8.2. What is the percentage of people in agriculture and the number of calories per person in (a) Switzerland, (b) Brazil, (c) Sudan?
10. Draw a scattergraph to show the information in Figure 8.5.

Country	Income per person ($)	Adult literacy (%)
Chad	690	34
India	1,410	74
Algeria	4,470	70
Fiji	3,720	93
Lebanon	9,140	87
St Lucia	6,820	90
Hungary	12,730	99
Oman	19,260	81

Figure 8.5

National 5

1. What is the relationship between social indicators of development and economic indicators?
2. Describe the advantages of combined indicators of development over economic or social indicators.
3. In what ways are the Physical Quality of Life Index and the Human Development Index similar and different?
4. From the information in Figure 8.4:
   (a) Do you think the PQLI and the HDI give similar results?
   (b) Which is more reliable? Give reasons for your answer.
5. Look at Figure 8.1. What is the relationship between income per person and life expectancy? Give examples.
6. Look at Figure 8.2. What is the relationship between calories per person per day and percentage of people in agriculture? Give examples.
7. (a) Draw a scattergraph to show the information in Figure 8.6.
   (b) Describe the relationship shown by the scattergraph.

National 5 continued...

Country	GNP per person ($)	Population per doctor
Guyana	3,333	4,800
Morocco	3,084	2,000
Tonga	4,221	1,800
Tunisia	4,317	750
Turkey	10,363	750
Mexico	10,146	500
Uruguay	13,866	270
Georgia	3,210	240

Figure 8.6

Activities

1 high GNP per capita	2 low GNP per capita	3 many people employed in agriculture
4 few people employed in agriculture	5 high infant mortality rate	6 low infant mortality rate
7 high life expectancy	8 low life expectancy	9 high adult literacy
10 low adult literacy	11 many patients per doctor	12 few patients per doctor
13 many children attending school	14 few children attending school	15 a lot of energy used per person
16 little energy used per person	17 PQLI	18 HDI

1. Examine each of the terms in the table above. Make sure that you understand what each of the terms means.
2. Now look at the table below. There are ten rows. The numbers refer to the terms above.
   (a) For each row, decide which of the three terms is the odd one out.
   (b) State why it is the odd one out.
   Group A has been done for you as an example. Remember, it is your explanation that is important here.
       9 = high adult literacy   7 = high life expectancy   2 = low GNP per capita

   All three terms are to do with development but 'low GNP per capita' is the odd one out because the other two terms are to do with development in developed countries.

Group			
A	9	7	2
B	1	3	12
C	12	15	10
D	6	7	14
E	13	4	11
F	18	17	1
G	17	7	1
H	18	9	15
I	16	8	15
J	11	14	15

Now complete the 'I can do' boxes for this chapter.

Chapter 9

Reasons for differences in development levels (1)

This chapter looks at physical reasons for differences in levels of development.

By the end of this chapter, you should be able to:

✓ list some differences between developed and developing countries
✓ list some of the physical factors affecting development
✓ explain how physical factors affect development.

Global variations in development

By using one or more development indicator, the world can be divided into **developed or economically more developed countries** (EMDCs) and **developing or economically less developed countries** (ELDCs). These are shown in Figure 9.1. The developed countries are fewer in number, nearly all are in the northern hemisphere, and most are in temperate latitudes. The developing countries have 75 per cent of the world's people. They are found in both the northern and southern hemispheres and they include all the countries within the tropics.

Figure 9.1 also shows that there are big differences in living standards *within* developing countries. For example, the average income in South America is 6 times that in Africa and people can expect to live 16 years longer. And, within the continent of Africa, people of Libya earn 50 times more than the people of the Democratic Republic of Congo and live 30 years longer.

There are many reasons for the huge variations in standards of living around the world. The factors involved can be divided into physical and human. In this chapter we examine physical factors.

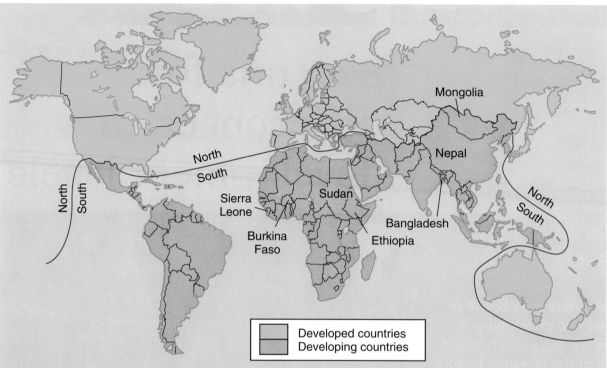

Continent	GNP / person ($)	Life expectancy	% Attending secondary school
North America	32,077	79	99
South America	9,024	74	92
Europe	25,434	77	00
Asia	2,941	70	85
Africa	1,576	58	69
Oceania	39,052	77	92

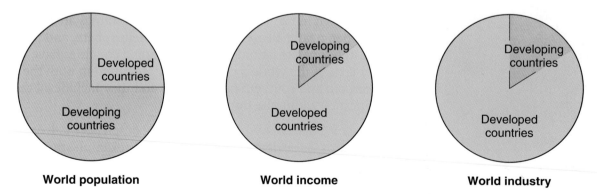

Figure 9.1
Developed and developing countries

Physical factors

Factor	Problem	Why this is a problem	Example
Climate	Very cold	• Difficult to build roads and railways • Remote and unlikely to attract much industry • Too cold to farm • Expensive to live because high heating bills, food is expensive • Houses difficult to build because of permafrost	Mongolia
	Very dry	• Barely enough rain to grow crops • Always at risk of crop failure and famine • Remote and unlikely to attract industry • Soil made poorer by wind erosion	Ethiopia
Relief	Very steep	• Difficult to build roads and railways, so remote and unlikely to attract much industry • Poor farming because of steep land, inability to use machinery and thin soils	Nepal
Resources	Lack of minerals	• No valuable minerals (e.g. diamonds, gold) to sell to other countries • No fuels (e.g. coal, oil) to encourage industry to set up	Malawi
Environment	Unattractive scenery	• Not attractive to summer tourists (e.g. no sandy beaches, hot, sunny climate) or winter tourists (e.g. no cold, snowy, steep slopes)	Burkina Faso
	Much disease	• A country is unable to develop if many of its people suffer from disease and are unable to work properly	Sierra Leone
Natural disasters	Floods, drought, earthquakes, volcanic eruptions, hurricanes	• Areas prone to natural disasters have harvests ruined, factories and homes destroyed, roads and railways unusable • Costs millions of pounds and may cause famine and unemployment • May take years for areas to recover	Bangladesh

National 4

1. Name two continents that consist entirely of developing countries.
2. Name three continents that consist entirely of developed countries.
3. 'Developing countries are all equally poor.'
   Is this statement true? Give reasons for your answer.
4. Explain how its climate can affect the development of a country.
5. Why is relief such an important factor in development levels?
6. Explain how countries' resources help to explain differences in development.
7. Look at the following list of physical problems:
   very cold   very dry   mountainous   prone to severe earthquakes
   suffers from frequent eruptions   affected by frequent hurricanes
   Which of these problems do you think a country finds easiest and which most difficult to overcome? Give reasons for your answers.

National 5

1. Describe the world distribution of economically less developed countries.
2. 'Developing countries are all equally poor.'
   Is this statement true? Give reasons for your answer.
3. Explain, in detail, how climate can affect the development of a country.
4. Why do countries such as Nepal find it difficult to develop?
5. Explain, in detail, how resources and environment help to explain differences in standards of living around the world.
6. Look at the following list of physical problems:
   very cold   very dry   mountainous   prone to severe earthquakes
   suffers from frequent eruptions   affected by frequent hurricanes
   Which of these problems do you think a country finds easiest and which most difficult to overcome? Give reasons for your answers.

Activities

Look carefully at the pictures below showing different types of landscape. Make sure you understand exactly what each picture is showing you.

1. For each picture, write down what it is about this landscape that makes development so difficult.
2. Try to think of at least one country that would have each of the different problems.

A

B

C

D

E

F

Now complete the 'I can do' boxes for this chapter.

Chapter 10

Reasons for differences in development levels (2)

This chapter looks at the human reasons for differences in levels of development.

By the end of this chapter, you should be able to:

✓ describe the impact of population growth on development
✓ explain the connection between industrialisation and development
✓ give reasons why trade has an impact on development.

Human factors

Some countries find it difficult to develop because of their physical environment, but there are many states that have overcome the problems of a harsh environment and enjoy a high standard of living. Such countries include Japan, Finland, Switzerland, Canada and Australia. There must, therefore, be other factors – human factors – that help to explain differences in development levels around the world. Some of the most important of these are described below.

	Developing world	Developed world
Average birth rate (per 1,000 people)	22	10
Average death rate (per 1,000 people)	8	8
Average natural increase (% of population)	14	2

Figure 10.1
Comparing human factors in the developed and developing world

Population growth

As Figure 10.1 shows, **population is rising seven times faster in developing than in developed countries.** This gives poorer countries two sets of problems.

In the countryside, **farms become smaller**, as there are more people needing land. So the farmers produce less food for their families to eat and have an increased risk of going hungry.

In the cities, **the city authorities cannot provide enough houses, schools, hospital beds and jobs for the increasing population**. So many people live in makeshift houses (*shanty towns*), are underemployed and have little chance of getting to a hospital if they are ill. In Tanzania in East Africa, for example, there are 50,000 people to every doctor.

Because the birth rate is still high, there are many young children in developing countries. In Niger, for instance, over half of the people are 14 years old or younger. **This large number of children places an additional strain on the country.** The children do not produce wealth, but they need to be kept healthy, well fed, educated and properly clothed.

Industrialisation

	Developing world	Developed world

% people working in:
   agriculture
   manufacturing
   services
	45
	23
	32
		3
		27
		70

% of world's industry	15	85

Figure 10.2
Comparing the developing and developed worlds in terms of industry

As Figure 10.2 shows, **there are far fewer factories and offices in developing countries than in developed countries**. Factories and offices produce profits that increase a country's wealth. They also employ many people, providing them with a regular wage. Without industry, a country finds it very difficult to develop.

In addition, although there is little industry, the population in developing world cities is rising rapidly. This means that more and more people are unemployed or underemployed and have only a low standard of living.

Factories and offices are less likely to set up in developing countries because there are few people there who are rich enough to buy their products. So the goods have to be transported great distances to be sold, which increases costs. The roads and railways are also poorer and there are fewer banks from which to borrow money. With fewer secondary schools and universities, there are not many people with the necessary skills (e.g. in information technology) to work in a modern office. Although some industries are found in poorer countries, they are often foreign-owned (*multi-national companies*), so the profits do not stay in that country to increase its wealth.

	Developed world	Developing world
Imports	Manufactured and primary goods	Expensive manufactured goods
Exports	Expensive manufactured goods	Cheap primary goods
Trade balance	Trade surplus	Trade deficit
Debts	Lend money to poorer nations	Borrow money at high interest rates

Figure 10.3
Comparing the developing and developed worlds in terms of trade

Trade

As Figure 10.3 shows, with few factories, **most developing countries have only primary goods to export** (such as crops and minerals). **Their prices are generally low** and also fluctuate greatly. For example, in 2012 the price farmers received for coffee was half the price they had received the year before. **Developing countries need to import manufactured goods, but they are expensive** and generally rise in price. So the money they receive from their exports does not usually pay for their imports. This means **they cannot afford to provide enough services** (e.g. hospital equipment, school books, agricultural machinery) to enable people to enjoy a higher standard of living. It also means that, over the years, they have borrowed large amounts of money from developed countries and now **spend much of their income just in repaying interest on these debts**. This is money that otherwise would have been spent on improving people's standard of living.

Developing countries even find it difficult to export the few goods that they do produce. This is because other countries put up *trade barriers* to protect their own industries. So developing countries may find that they are only allowed to export a limited number of goods to countries such as the USA (a *quota*) or find that a tax or *tariff* is put on their goods so that their price is too high for people to buy.

National 4

1. Describe the differences in birth rates and death rates in developed and developing countries.
2. In what ways does an increasing population cause problems for a developing country:
   (a) in the countryside?
   (b) in the cities?
3. Give two reasons why factories are less likely to set up in developing countries.
4. (a) Describe the type of goods that developing countries export.
   (b) What problems does this bring to developing countries?
5. (a) Describe the type of goods that developing countries import.
   (b) Are these goods more or less expensive than the goods they export?
   (c) What problem does this cause?
6. Why do developing countries find it difficult to export the few goods that they do produce?
7. For a typical developing country, which of the following would do most to improve the standard of living of its people?
   • Halve the birth rate
   • Double its exports
   • Double its factories
   Give reasons for your answer.

National 5

1. Compare birth rates, death rates and natural increase in developed and developing countries.
2. How do population problems explain the low level of development in developing countries?
3. Give four reasons why fewer factories set up in developing countries.
4. Explain why countries with many factories and offices can enjoy a higher standard of living.
5. Compare imports and exports in developed and developing countries.
6. Give one reason why most developing countries are in debt and explain how this affects their development.
7. How do trade problems explain the low level of development in poorer countries?
8. For a typical developing country, which of the following would do most to improve the standard of living of its people?
   - Halve the birth rate
   - Double its exports
   - Double its factories

   Give reasons for your answer.

Activities

Read through the statements below showing some of the human reasons for differences in development levels. The information in some of the statements is not correct. You should re-write these statements with the correct information.

1. Physical factors, such as climate and relief, are the only factors in explaining differences in development.
2. Population is rising more slowly in developing countries than in developed countries.
3. Countries with problems caused by rapid population growth are more likely to be developed countries.
4. In the countryside in developing countries, as population increases, farms become smaller as there are fewer people needing the land.
5. In the cities in developing countries, authorities cannot provide enough houses, schools, hospitals and jobs for the increasing population.
6. Countries that have the majority of people working in agriculture are more likely to be developing countries.
7. Factories and offices are more likely to set up in developing countries because there are many people there rich enough to buy their products.
8. Roads and railways are much better in developing countries, which attracts industry.
9. There are fewer secondary schools and universities in developing countries so there are not very many people with the necessary skills to work in modern offices.
10. Most developing countries have only primary goods to export. The prices of these are generally low and fluctuate greatly.
11. Developing countries need to import manufactured goods that are very cheap.
12. Developing countries suffer from trade deficits, where they spend more on imports than they make on their exports.

Now complete the 'I can do' boxes for this chapter.

Chapter 11

Land uses in developed world cities

By the end of this chapter, you should be able to:

✓ understand why cities grow
✓ list the main land uses in a developed city
✓ understand one land use model of a developed city.

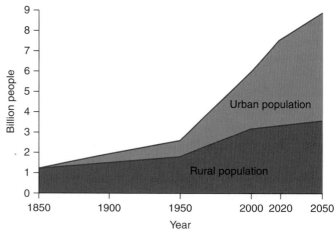

Figure 11.1
Growth in world urban and rural populations

The 7 billion people who live on this planet are not evenly spread out. We prefer to live in some areas much more than others. Increasingly we prefer to live in towns and cities. One hundred years ago, fewer than 200 million people lived in urban areas; now the urban population is 3500 million. But villages only grow into towns if there are reasons for people to move there, and this is usually because there are more job opportunities. There may be jobs in factories, offices, shops, services, ports and even hotels. These are called the town's functions: industrial centre, service centre, port, tourist resort and so on. As a settlement takes on new functions, more people move there and it grows.

When it is still a village nearly all the buildings in the settlement are houses. But, as it starts to grow, it develops other land use zones. It will have industrial areas, as well as new residential areas, and the old village will be taken over by shops and businesses and become the town centre or central business district (CBD).

A typical town grows out from its original village in all directions and its different land use zones can be shown as concentric zones, as in Figure 11.2.

These zones are constantly changing in character: old buildings are knocked down, new ones constructed and others just change their use. A better model of urban land use is shown in Figure 11.3. It shows some of the big changes taking place in a city. These will be studied in more detail in Chapters 13–18, on Glasgow.

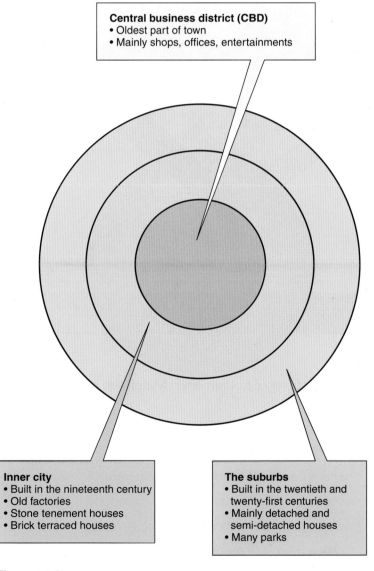

Central business district (CBD)
• Oldest part of town
• Mainly shops, offices, entertainments

Inner city
• Built in the nineteenth century
• Old factories
• Stone tenement houses
• Brick terraced houses

The suburbs
• Built in the twentieth and twenty-first centuries
• Mainly detached and semi-detached houses
• Many parks

Figure 11.2
Urban land use zones

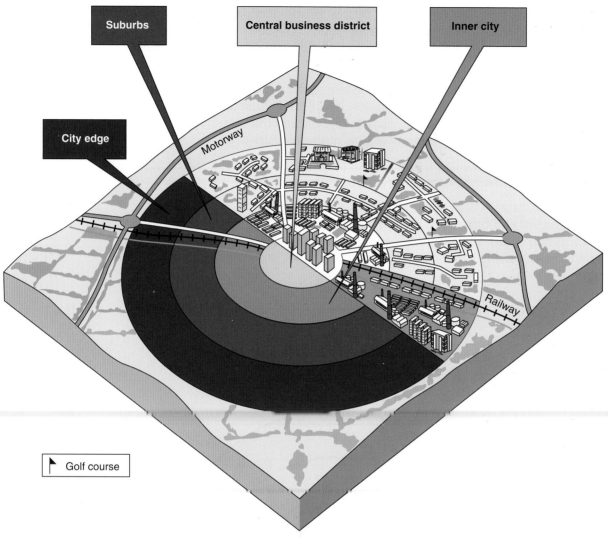

Figure 11.3
Changes to urban land use zones

Activities

Activity A

The list below shows the main functions of settlements. Match the settlement function with its correct definition.

Industrial centre	where ships load and unload goods
Market centre	where there are many jobs in factories and offices
Service centre	where people live but work elsewhere
Tourist resort	where farmers buy and sell their produce
Commuter centre	where many senior citizens choose to live
Retirement centre	where there are many jobs in shops, entertainments
Port	where people go on holiday

Activities continued...

Activity B

Which of the functions listed in Activity A does your local town have (or has had in the past)?

Activity C

Re-write the paragraph below, putting in each of the correct settlement functions.

Settlements easy for local farmers to reach have been _____ centres for hundreds of years. At that time there was some fishing and trading abroad, so small _____ developed. In the nineteenth century many towns grew rapidly as _____ centres. In the twentieth century as people became wealthier _____ centres grew. People also went on holiday so _____ centres grew. Now many people prefer to live in villages away from their place of work and _____ centres have grown up. And, as people live longer, quieter places have become _____ centres.

Now complete the 'I can do' boxes for this chapter.

Chapter 12

Land use zones in developed world cities

> This chapter looks at the different land use zones in developed world cities.

By the end of this chapter, you should be able to:

- ✓ list the four main land use zones in a developed city
- ✓ list several characteristics of each zone
- ✓ understand some of the reasons for those characteristics.

Central business district

Figure 12.1

Characteristics

- Usually the oldest area, with many churches
- Where main roads meet
- High order shops and entertainments
- Hotels and tourist facilities
- Office blocks
- Tallest buildings
- Most densely packed buildings

Changes

- More indoor shopping malls
- Changes to road system
- More pedestrianised streets

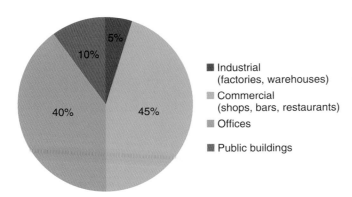

- Industrial (factories, warehouses)
- Commercial (shops, bars, restaurants)
- Offices
- Public buildings

Figure 12.2
Land uses in the central business district

Explanation

- Most accessible area of the city
- Most expensive land
  → mostly shops and offices
  → few houses
  → very tall buildings
  → little open space

Inner city

Figure 12.3

Characteristics

- Dates from the nineteenth century
- Straight rows of tenement or terraced houses
- Few gardens or small gardens
- Old factories, docks, warehouses
- Low order shops and services
- 3–4 storey housing and tall factories
- High density of buildings

Changes

- Decline of shops and services
- Old factories closing down
- Old housing replaced, at first by high-rise flats
- New terraced housing being built

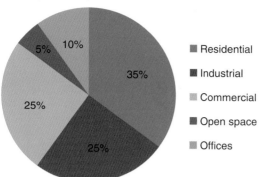

- Residential
- Industrial
- Commercial
- Open space
- Offices

Figure 12.4
Land use in the inner city

Explanation

- Quite accessible area of the city
  → factories
- Quite expensive land
  → high-density housing
  → quite tall buildings
  → little open space

City edge

Figure 12.5

Characteristics

- Dates from late twentieth century onwards
- Planned shopping centres
- Business and office parks
- Some detached housing
- Low density of buildings
- Much green space
- Beside main roads
- Much car parking
- Mostly 1–2 storey buildings

Changes

Building outwards into the countryside

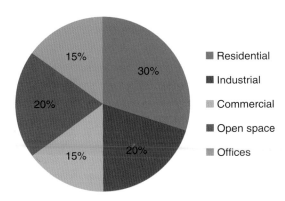

- Residential
- Industrial
- Commercial
- Open space
- Offices

15%
30%
20%
15%
20%

Figure 12.6
Land use at the city edge

Explanation

- Accessible area of the city
  → shopping centres and business parks
- Quite cheap land
  → space for landscaping, car parks
  → buildings with few storeys

Suburbs

Figure 12.7

Characteristics

- Dates from the twentieth century
- Semi-detached and detached houses
- Some low-rise and high-rise flats
- Many houses with large gardens
- Many houses with garages
- 1–2 storey housing
- Low density of buildings
- Much green space, e.g. parks, golf courses

Changes

- Least change here
- Improvements to low-rise and high-rise flats
- Traffic calming measures

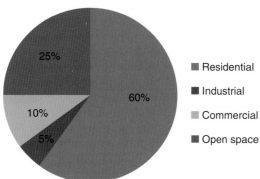

- Residential
- Industrial
- Commercial
- Open space

Explanation

- Quiet area of the city
  → few factories and shops
- The cheapest land
  → space for gardens, parks
- Popular place for families to live

Figure 12.8
Land use in the suburbs

National 4

1. Look at the pie-charts for the CBD and inner city (Figures 12.2 and 12.4). Which zone has the greater amount of (a) residential land use, (b) industrial, (c) commercial and (d) open space?
2. Compare the land uses in the suburbs and city edge (Figures 12.6 and 12.8) in the same ways.
3. Compare inner city housing with suburban housing.
4. Describe two ways in which the characteristics of the CBD and city edge are similar.
5. Compare the height and density of buildings in the inner city and city edge.
6. (a) Is the most expensive land in a city more important for shops or for housing?
   (b) Is the cheapest land in a city more important for shops or for housing?

National 5

1. Compare the importance of the different land uses in:
   (a) the CBD and inner city.
   (b) the suburbs and city edge.
2. Compare the characteristics of the housing in the inner city, suburbs and city edge.
3. Compare the characteristics of the CBD and city edge.
4. Describe the changes in (a) the height and (b) the density of buildings from the CBD to the city edge.
5. What is the connection between the price of land and (a) the number of shops and (b) the amount of housing?

Activities

Activity A

Draw a table similar to the one below. Then rank the four land use zones according to:

(a) the number of pedestrians there
(b) the number of cars parked on the street
(c) the amount of pollution
(d) the number of buildings with chimneys
(e) the number of bus stops
(f) the number of schools
(g) the amount of crime.

(Rank number 1 = the highest.)

	CBD	Inner city	Suburbs	City edge
Number of pedestrians				
Amount of street parking				
Amount of pollution				
Number of chimneys				
Number of bus stops				
Number of schools				
Amount of crime				

Activity B

Student at university in the city centre; also works part-time in a bar
Figure 12.9

Retired couple who do not drive

Family of five: father's job involves travel, mother is at home, children aged 3, 8 and 13

Young professional couple with a lot of disposable income

In which part of a city would the people above prefer to live: (a) CBD, (b) inner city or (c) suburbs? Give reasons for your answers.

Now complete the 'I can do' boxes for this chapter.

Chapter 13

This chapter looks at the growth of Glasgow.

Case study of a developed city: Glasgow, Scotland

By the end of this chapter, you should be able to:

✓ know how Glasgow's population has changed over time
✓ understand some of the reasons why Glasgow has grown
✓ understand how Glasgow's land use zones developed.

Year	Population
600	50
700	100
800	150
900	200
1000	500
1100	800
1200	1,400
1300	1,500
1400	1,500
1500	2,900
1600	7,000
1700	12,000
1750	32,000
1800	44,000
1850	329,000
1900	762,000
1950	1,090,000
2000	578,000
2012	600,000

Figure 13.1
Changes in Glasgow's population

Glasgow is Scotland's largest city but it is only in the last two hundred years that it has overtaken Edinburgh to become the biggest. Its growth is shown in Figures 13.1 and 13.2. As the city grew, it developed land use zones typical of a city in a developed country – see Figure 13.5.

Glasgow's original site

Glasgow has been settled for many hundreds of years. **The original settlement was beside a tributary of the River Clyde.** Here there was fresh water, wood for fuel and building, shelter, reasonable farmland and a site that was quite easy to defend.

Medieval Glasgow

Glasgow grew slowly as a religious centre. Its cathedral is 900 years old and it was a place of pilgrimage in early times. **It then became a market centre**, being at a crossing-point on the Clyde and easy for local people to reach. It remained a small market town until the eighteenth century.

The 1700s and 1800s

Then the Clyde was deepened and straightened so that ships could use it. **It became a port**, importing tobacco, cotton and sugar from North America and the West Indies. These imports led to Glasgow building its first factories – sugar refineries and cotton mills. People began to move here for work.

The factories needed coal for power and Glasgow had supplies of coal and ironstone, so there were many mining jobs. With coal and ironstone, the factories could make iron and later steel. With iron and steel and deep water, they could build ships. And with iron and steel and coal for power, they could make engines for the ships and locomotives and other heavy engineering goods. Many of these were exported through the new port of Glasgow, which created even more jobs. By 1900 the city had grown to 760,000 people. It was known as 'the second city of the British Empire' and became one of the biggest industrial centres in the world.

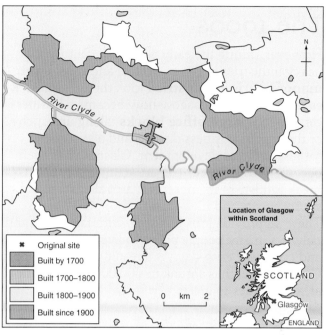

Figure 13.2
Age zones of Glasgow

Figure 13.3
Glasgow's Tolbooth

The 1900s

However, during the early twentieth century the heavy industries began to decline and **new light manufacturing industries** took their place. As well as making goods Glasgow now became a business centre, with **large office blocks** taking up much of the central business district, and also a centre for research and development. Glasgow has even become **a tourist centre**, attracting many short-break tourists to its museums, art galleries, major sports events and high-quality shopping centres. These all provide jobs but now, with fast roads and railways, many people prefer to live outside the city and commute each day. As a result the population of Glasgow itself has shrunk to 600,000 but its built-up area continues to grow.

Glasgow's land use zones

As Glasgow grew, the people started to move out of **the original core area**. This was where the main routes met and, being the most accessible area, it **became the central business district**. When Glasgow's population increased rapidly in **the 1800s, tenement houses and factories** were built around this original core. This **has become the inner city**. Wealthier factory managers and owners also lived in the inner city but in separate areas and in bigger houses. During the 1900s, as transport improved, many people moved out to the less polluted suburbs. Now development is still going on at the city's edge.

Figure 13.4
Glasgow's shipyards in 1951

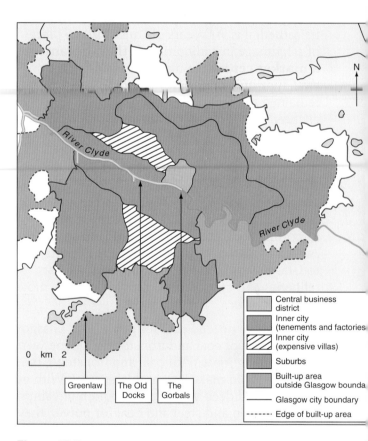

Figure 13.5
Land use zones of Glasgow

National 4

1. Why did so many people move to Glasgow in the 1700s and 1800s?
2. Why did people move to the suburbs in the 1900s?
3. What are the main types of jobs in Glasgow now?
4. Why has the population of Glasgow been decreasing recently?
5. Why did the original core of Glasgow become the CBD?
6. Which land use zone in Glasgow:
   (a) is the most recent?
   (b) was built in the nineteenth century?

National 5

1. Glasgow's earliest function was as a religious centre. Name four important functions it has had since that time.
2. When did Glasgow's population grow fastest? Why?
3. When did Glasgow's population start to decrease? Why?
4. Explain how Glasgow's land use zones have developed.

Activities

When do you think these events happened? Choose the most likely date.

1. Population of Glasgow reaches 1 million — 1930 or 1990

2. Unemployment in Glasgow reaches 50 per cent — 1930 or 1990

3. Glasgow builds one-fifth of all the ships in the world — 1800 or 1900

4. Glasgow expands as far as the Clyde — 1100 or 1800

5. The Tolbooth in Glasgow is built — 1600 or 1900

6. Glasgow's tourist information centre expands — 1890 or 1990

7. Drovers bring their cattle to Glasgow — 1100 or 1600

8. Many sandstone quarries open near Glasgow — 1850 or 1950

9. Many 'tobacco lords' can be seen in their red cloaks — 1550 or 1750

10. Glasgow expands rapidly into the countryside — 1800 or 2000

Now complete the 'I can do' boxes for this chapter.

Chapter

14

Changes in Glasgow's CBD

By the end of this chapter, you should be able to:

- ✓ understand the reasons for traffic congestion in Glasgow's CBD
- ✓ describe several effects of and solutions to traffic congestion here
- ✓ describe and explain some of the main shopping changes.

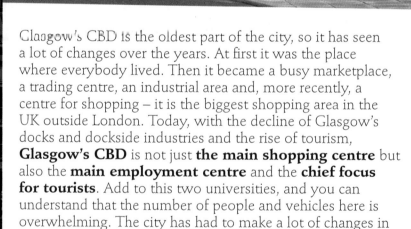

Glasgow's CBD is the oldest part of the city, so it has seen a lot of changes over the years. At first it was the place where everybody lived. Then it became a busy marketplace, a trading centre, an industrial area and, more recently, a centre for shopping – it is the biggest shopping area in the UK outside London. Today, with the decline of Glasgow's docks and dockside industries and the rise of tourism, **Glasgow's CBD** is not just **the main shopping centre** but also the **main employment centre** and the **chief focus for tourists**. Add to this two universities, and you can understand that the number of people and vehicles here is overwhelming. The city has had to make a lot of changes in order to cope.

Transport changes

Many of the people coming into the city centre prefer to drive, and many main roads lead into the centre. The roads in the centre are in a grid-iron pattern with many intersections, which need traffic lights. This holds up traffic, as do all the buses, pedestrians and delivery lorries. This is bad for business: deliveries arrive late, people are late getting to work, and emergency services are delayed. It frustrates drivers, increases road accidents, and the exhaust fumes from stationary vehicles increase air pollution to a dangerous level. Glasgow has tried many solutions over the years, some of which are shown in Figure 14.1.

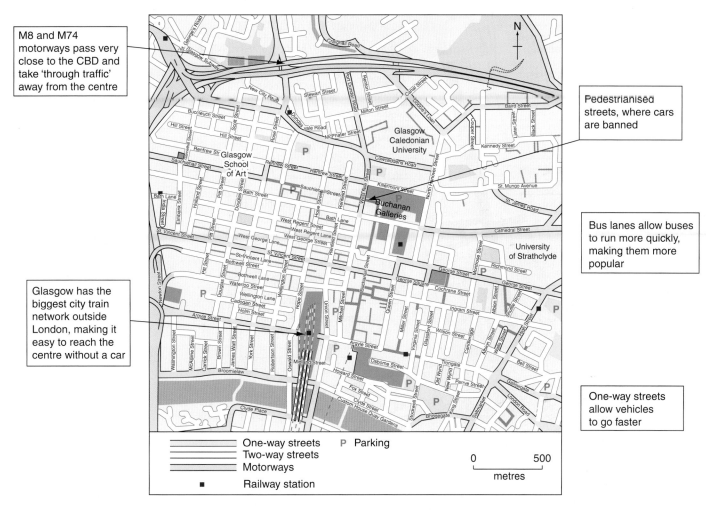

Figure 14.1
Solutions to traffic congestion in Glasgow's CBD

Shopping changes

In the last fifteen years several large indoor shopping centres have been set up outside the city's CBD. These are very popular, with many high-street shops all under one roof and free and plentiful car parking. Braehead shopping centre, for example, has over 120 shops and 300,000 customers per week, while Silverburn shopping centre has 130 shops and 500,000 customers per week. The sudden growth of these centres has forced the city centre to make substantial changes to its shopping area. These are shown in Figure 14.2.

14

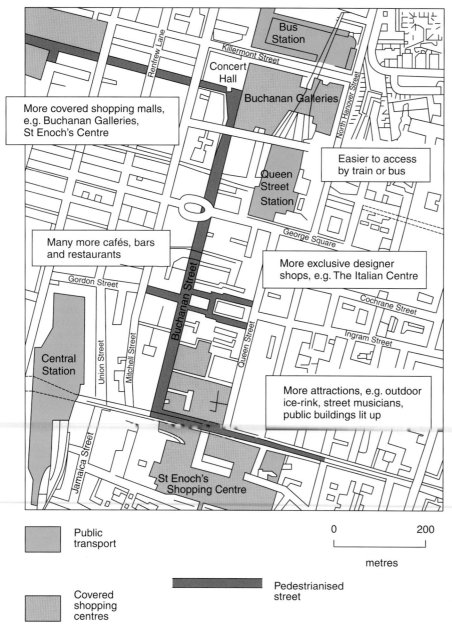

More covered shopping malls, e.g. Buchanan Galleries, St Enoch's Centre

Easier to access by train or bus

Many more cafés, bars and restaurants

More exclusive designer shops, e.g. The Italian Centre

More attractions, e.g. outdoor ice-rink, street musicians, public buildings lit up

Public transport

Covered shopping centres

Pedestrianised street

0   200

metres

Figure 14.2
The main shopping area in Glasgow's CBD

National 4

1. Why is there so much traffic in the centre of Glasgow?
2. What causes congestion in the city centre?
3. In your opinion, what is the worst effect of traffic congestion? Give a reason for your answer.
4. Buses and cars both use the roads. So why are people encouraged to travel by bus instead of by car?
5. What solutions make it easier to drive a car in the city centre?
6. Name two shopping changes in Glasgow's city centre. For each one, explain how it improves the centre for shoppers.

National 5

1. Why is there so much traffic in the centre of Glasgow?
2. What causes congestion in the city centre?
3. Explain the ways in which traffic congestion can be dangerous.
4. Which solutions to congestion make it easier to drive in the city centre and which solutions persuade people not to drive in the centre?
5. Five improvements to city centre shopping are given in Figure 14.2. Rank them according to how much difference you think they make. Give reasons for your decisions.

Activities

'I didn't think of that.'

1. When planners make improvements to our cities, they have to be very careful that there are no side-effects or knock-on effects. For example, banning cars from streets makes it safer for shoppers. But can you think of any disadvantages? (Clues: different groups of people, roads nearby …)
2. Buchanan Galleries is a very popular new shopping mall in the middle of the CBD, with many shops, including John Lewis, and its own car park underneath. Can you think of any bad side-effects of its popularity? (Clues: other shops, queues …)
3. Which of these solutions to traffic congestion has the most serious disadvantages, do you think: bus lanes, urban motorways or one-way streets? Explain why.

Now complete the 'I can do' boxes for this chapter.

Chapter 15

Changes in Glasgow's inner city (1)

> This chapter looks at recent changes in the inner city area of the Gorbals.

By the end of this chapter, you should be able to:

✓ describe the problems in the Gorbals area of Glasgow in the 1950s
✓ describe some recent changes in the Gorbals
✓ describe how these changes have improved the Gorbals.

During the 1800s, Glasgow's population grew by 700,000, which is an extra 7000 people every year. Hundreds of blocks of tenements were built to house everyone and they had to be built close together, within walking distance of the docks, shipyards and factories where nearly everyone worked. In the early 1900s, as more people continued to flood into Glasgow, many of the tenement flats were divided up. For instance, one three-room flat would become three separate one-room flats. By the 1950s the inner city had become seriously overcrowded. At the same time many of the shipyards and factories began to close down. The inner city was in urgent need of help. The Council prioritised the different inner city areas according to the level of deprivation and set about making improvements, a process that still continues today. Inner city Glasgow covers a very large area, and different areas have undergone different changes. Two of these areas are examined here in more detail.

Changes in the Gorbals

Figure 13.5 shows the location of the Gorbals, next to the CBD just south of the River Clyde, an area of little more than 1 km². In the 1950s it was the number one priority area for development. Its worst problems are shown in Figure 15.3.

Figure 15.1
The Gorbals in the 1950s

Figure 15.2
Crown Street in the Gorbals in the 1960s

Housing

The most overcrowded area in Europe with 90,000 people (in the 1930s)

People living in one-room or two-room flats with shared toilets

Environment

Air pollution a serious health hazard

No green space

Rubbish tips attracting rats

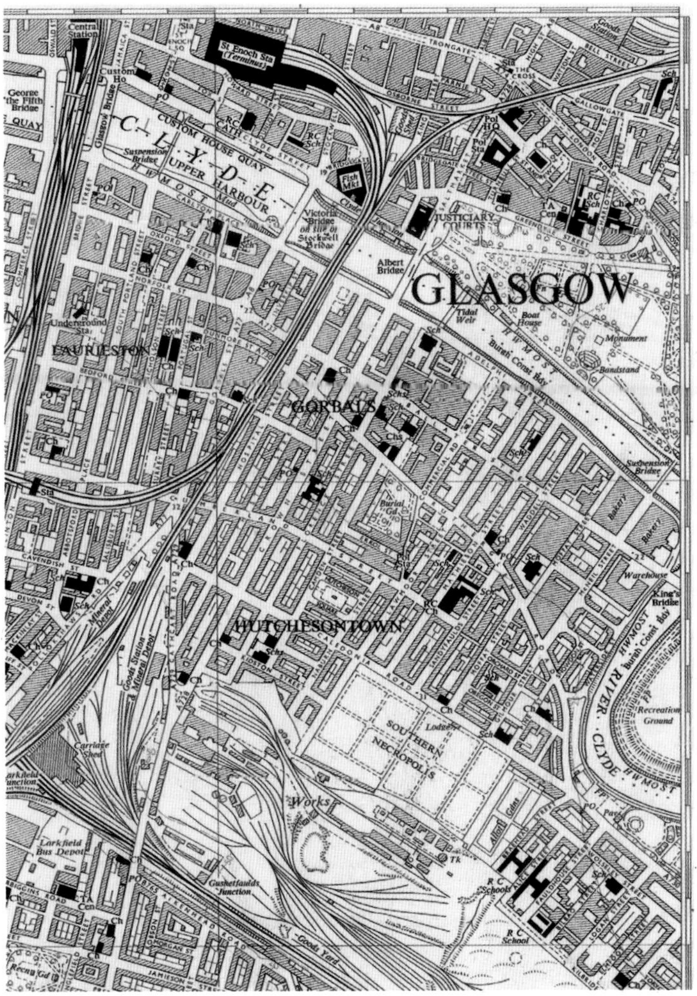

Services

Hundreds of small shops, pubs, churches and schools

Industry

Steelworks and other factories closing down

Figure 15.3
Problems in the Gorbals in the 1950s

The first solution to the Gorbals' housing problem was to pull down almost all the tenements and build high-rise flats. This solution allowed many people to still live in the Gorbals although a lot were rehoused to outer city estates. But many high-rise flats were poorly built, suffered from damp, had no space for children to play, and lacked neighbourliness. So, in the 1990s, a new regeneration scheme began.

The regeneration of the Gorbals, shown in Figures 15.4 and 15.5, has transformed the area. It still has economic and social problems but more and more people are moving in, the environment is much improved, and the image and reputation of the area is significantly better.

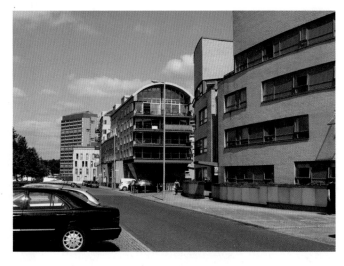

Figure 15.4
New Gorbals housing in foreground, 1960s high-rise flats in distance

Improved employment

New industrial estate set up on site of old steelworks

Hotel, college and other services all provide jobs

Improved environment

Houses now have private gardens

New park

Improved housing

New 2-storey brick tenements built

Some new houses for sale (not just for renting), attracting a wider social mix

Some high-rise flats pulled down

Improved services

New library, health centre, leisure centre

Figure 15.5
Improvements in the Gorbals
© Crown copyright 2013. All rights reserved. Ordnance Survey licence number 100047450.

National 4

1. Why were Glasgow's tenements built so close together?
2. Why were many of the flats divided up?
3. Glasgow City Council started to redevelop its inner city in the 1950s. Explain why.
4. Look at Figure 15.3 which shows some of the problems in the Gorbals in the 1950s. Describe:
   (a) one employment problem
   (b) two housing problems, and
   (c) two environmental problems.
5. Explain why building high-rise flats was not successful in the Gorbals.
6. Look at Figure 15.5, which shows recent improvements in the Gorbals.
   Which improvement, do you think, has most helped to attract people back to live here? Give reasons for your answer.

National 5

1. Why is Glasgow's inner city so large?
2. Explain fully why Glasgow's inner city became overcrowded.
3. Describe the housing, employment and environmental problems faced by the Gorbals in the 1950s.
4. Figure 15.5 shows the recent regeneration scheme in the Gorbals.
   Which two improvements, do you think, have most helped to attract people back to live here? Explain fully.

Activities

Activity A

Imagine you were living in the Gorbals in the 1950s and you were campaigning for improvements. Design a banner to hold up during your protest march through Glasgow.

Activity B

Imagine you work for Glasgow City Council today and you want to attract more people to live in the Gorbals. Design a poster to be displayed around the city.

Figure 15.6

Now complete the 'I can do' boxes for this chapter.

Chapter 16

Changes in Glasgow's inner city (2)

This chapter looks at recent changes in the Old Docks inner city area.

By the end of this chapter, you should be able to:

✓ describe the problems in the Old Docks area of Glasgow in the 1960s
✓ describe some recent changes in the Old Docks
✓ describe how these changes have improved the Old Docks.

Much of Glasgow's inner city is unrecognisable from the way it looked in the 1960s. In some parts old tenements have been renovated or replaced by attractive new housing, such as in the Gorbals. In other parts the old factories have disappeared and, in their place, a new brand of industry has sprung up. These changes have been equally spectacular, no more so than in the Old Docks area of the city.

Changes in the Old Docks

Glasgow at one time had many docks which were busier than any port in the UK, apart from London, and its 50 or more shipyards were world-famous. Today the inner city has just two shipyards and one dock.

When the shipyards and docks closed down, **the area had to be reclaimed** before it could be used again. The shipyards and warehouses were dismantled, the docks filled in, areas of grass and trees were planted and everywhere was given a facelift in order to attract new developments. Figure 16.1 is a map showing the Old Docks before redevelopment.

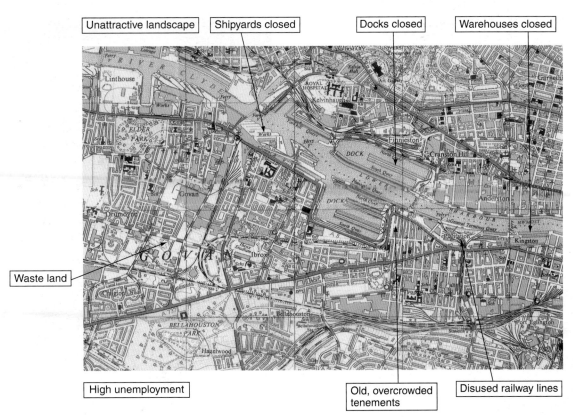

Unattractive landscape

Shipyards closed

Docks closed

Warehouses closed

Waste land

High unemployment

Old, overcrowded tenements

Disused railway lines

Figure 16.1
The Old Docks in the 1970s

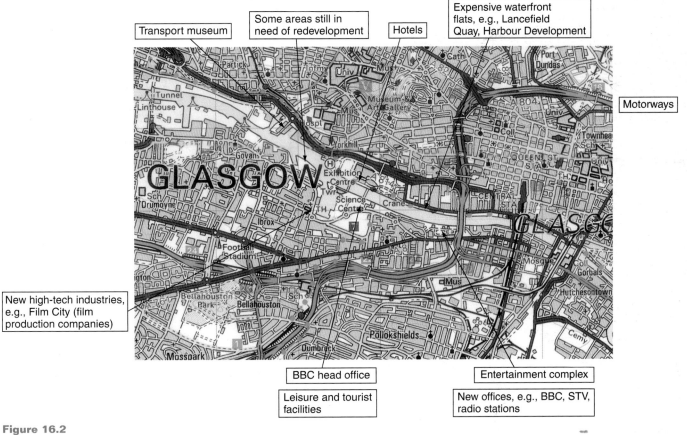

Transport museum

Some areas still in need of redevelopment

Hotels

Expensive waterfront flats, e.g., Lancefield Quay, Harbour Development

Motorways

New high-tech industries, e.g., Film City (film production companies)

BBC head office

Leisure and tourist facilities

Entertainment complex

New offices, e.g., BBC, STV, radio stations

Figure 16.2
Recent developments in the Old Docks
© Crown copyright 2013. All rights reserved. Ordnance Survey licence number 100047450.

The Old Docks is an example of a brownfield site, an area where old industry has been replaced by new development. These developments are different from those in the Gorbals. The new buildings reflect the ways in which people in Glasgow now make a living. No longer do Glaswegians work in heavy manufacturing industries. Today, most people work in offices and in the entertainment and tourist sectors. Some of these new industries can be seen in the Old Docks, together with a lot of new housing. The main changes are shown in Figure 16.2.

Figure 16.3
Some of the new developments in the Old Docks area

National 4

1. Look at Figure 16.1. Apart from being used for docks, in what other ways was the land in the Old Docks area used?
2. Why was unemployment high in the 1960s?
3. What made the landscape unattractive?
4. What is a brownfield site?
5. Look at Figure 16.2. Give four examples of new developments in the Old Docks that are related to tourism.
6. Give two examples of new offices in the Old Docks area.

National 5

1. Explain fully why the Old Docks area of Glasgow needed to be reclaimed.
2. Describe the new types of employment in the Old Docks.
3. (a) Name two tourist attractions in the Old Docks area.
   (b) Explain why hotels and restaurants often locate near tourist attractions.

Activities

Activity A

Why shipyards set up in the Old Docks area

✓ Near their raw materials
✓ Near a large labour force
✓ Beside water
✓ On a large area of flat land
✓ Easy to reach by rail and road

The table above gives the main reasons why so many shipyards set up here over a hundred years ago. Now new industries such as the BBC have taken over.

1. Which of the reasons in the table might explain why the BBC set up here? Explain your answer.
2. Can you think of any other reasons?

Activity B

Imagine it is your job to turn a large area of derelict land into a popular area where companies will set up and people will live. What will you need to do? What will you need to build – apart from the houses? How should the area look? What type of houses will be built?

Figure 16.4

Now complete the 'I can do' boxes for this chapter.

Chapter 17

Changes in Glasgow's suburbs

This chapter looks at recent changes in Glasgow's suburbs.

By the end of this chapter, you should be able to:

- ✓ list some of the features of the Greenlaw development in Glasgow's suburbs
- ✓ explain why people want to move to Glasgow's suburbs
- ✓ explain why industry and shops want to move to Glasgow's suburbs.

Glasgow's suburbs are very popular – with people as places to live, and with businesses and shops. All these land uses need roads and the residents need services such as health centres and schools. They also need recreational areas, such as golf courses, and somewhere to dispose of their rubbish (landfill sites). All of this means that the city is growing outwards rapidly. The areas where this is happening most is called the *city edge* (see Figure 13.5 on page 58).

But what is so attractive about the suburbs? And does their popularity cause any problems?

Case study of Greenlaw, south-west Glasgow

Greenlaw Farm used to be a livestock farm just to the south-west of Glasgow and on Green Belt land. It no longer exists. It is now part of the built-up area of Glasgow. Building began in 2009.

Greenlaw housing

There is a mixture of housing at Greenlaw – some social housing (more affordable homes) and private houses. The houses are of different sizes to attract all age groups and income groups to the area.

Why people want to live in Greenlaw

- Quieter and less polluted than nearer the city centre
- Less crime than nearer the city centre
- At the edge of the countryside
- New, clean and attractive
- Local services – schools, health centre and shops
- Near a motorway junction
- Near a railway station
- Cheaper land so houses and gardens can be bigger

Other examples of new housing at the city edge in Glasgow can be found elsewhere, in Newton Mearns, at Robroyston and near Carmunnock.

Greenlaw industry

A new business park is due for completion in 2017. There is also other employment in a hotel and in amenities such as a pub, restaurants, a fitness centre and shops.

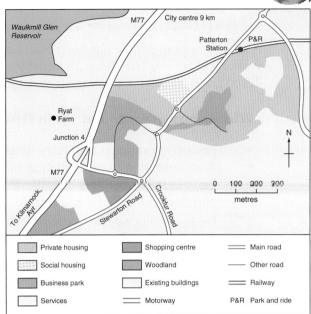

Figure 17.1
Greenlaw development, Glasgow

Why industry wants to set up in Greenlaw

- Land in the suburbs is cheaper to rent or buy
- Near a motorway junction, so easy for delivery lorries to reach
- Less road congestion than nearer the centre
- Near a railway station, so easy for workers to reach
- New, clean, crime-free, less polluted and a pleasant outlook provides an attractive environment for people to work in

Other examples of new industry at the city edge of Glasgow include the West of Scotland Science Park and Cambuslang Investment Park.

Figure 17.2
The Greenlaw development, looking to the north-west

Greenlaw shops

A new shopping parade has been built here for the benefit of people living and working close by. The shops are mostly convenience shops such as Waitrose and Tesco supermarkets, a newsagent and a pharmacy.

Why shops want to set up in Greenlaw

- Near customers in the many housing areas
- Also near many workers in the business park
- Land in the suburbs is cheaper to rent or buy so car parks can be large and free, attracting more people
- Near a motorway junction, so easy for customers and delivery lorries to reach
- Less road congestion than nearer the centre
- Clean, crime-free, less polluted and a pleasant outlook provides an attractive environment for people to shop

Other new shopping developments in Glasgow are now built within existing shopping centres rather than on greenfield sites.

National 4

1. New building developments are taking place at the edge of every city. Housing is one new land use found there. Name four other new land uses.
2. Greenlaw is in south-west Glasgow. How has it changed in recent years?
3. How do planners make sure there is a mix of people in a new housing area?
4. State four reasons why people want to live in Glasgow's suburbs.
5. Describe the type of environment in the suburbs that attracts shops and industry.
6. Why is it important for new industry and shopping centres to be near motorway junctions?
7. Explain how the price of the land in the suburbs attracts industry and shops to the suburbs.

National 5

1. New building developments are taking place at the edge of every city. Describe the new land uses found there.
2. Explain fully why many people prefer to live in the suburbs.
3. New developments at the city edge are often beside fast roads. Describe the advantages to residents, to businesses and to shops of being near fast roads.
4. Explain fully the advantages for industry of setting up at the city edge rather than near the city centre.

Activities

Activity A

Design a poster with a catchy slogan that will attract *either* people to live in Greenlaw *or* companies to set up in Greenlaw.

Figure 17.3

Activity B

The built-up area of Glasgow grows larger every year. It covers nearly twice the area it did 50 years ago. Do you think it will be even bigger in 20–30 years' time? Give reasons for your answer.

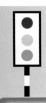

Now complete the 'I can do' boxes for this chapter.

Chapter 18

Conflicts in Glasgow's suburbs

This chapter looks at some recent conflicts in Glasgow's suburbs.

By the end of this chapter, you should be able to:

- ✓ understand what is meant by urban sprawl
- ✓ describe some good and bad effects of urban sprawl in Glasgow
- ✓ describe some solutions to urban sprawl in Glasgow.

Building on countryside at the edge of the suburbs is called *urban sprawl*. When any building development takes place, it has effects – both good and bad.

General effects of building in the suburbs

- More road traffic, more air and noise pollution
- Less farmland and less food produced
- Loss of trees, plant life and wildlife
- One development often leads to others
- Building developments reach villages which then become suburbs of Glasgow

Effects of more housing in the suburbs

- Fewer people live in the inner city and centre
- More commuters and so more vehicles travelling into the centre
- Even more development because more people need more services, such as health centres and schools

Effects of more industry in the suburbs

- Provides jobs for local people so less journey time to work
- These industries might otherwise have set up nearer the centre of Glasgow so this has reduced traffic and pollution there

Effects of more shops in the suburbs

- Very convenient for local people, so reduces their journey time to shops
- More competition for existing shops nearby
- Shopping centres selling comparison goods (e.g. clothes, shoes) will reduce the number of customers going into the city centre, so reducing congestion and air pollution there

Although new houses, business parks, shopping centres and golf courses cause problems, they bring many benefits to the people who use them. But one type of development, in particular, causes a lot of conflict with local people: landfill sites.

Cathkin landfill site

As a country we produce more rubbish now than ever before and much of it is buried at landfill sites. It is very expensive to transport such a lot of waste so the landfill site must be close to the edge of the city. But if it is near the edge of the city it is near where people live. This gives rise to conflicts.

Glasgow produces 350,000 tonnes of waste each year and 74 per cent is transported by large, heavy articulated lorries to Cathkin landfill site near Carmunnock. Cathkin landfill site was due to close in 2012 but it had its life extended until 2016, much to the annoyance of local people. The reasons why landfill sites annoy local people are shown in Figure 18.1.

Unpleasant smell

Rubbish can be blown into surrounding areas

Many lorries damage roads

Attracts vermin and seagulls

Looks ugly (visual pollution)

Swarms of flies gather, if not covered

It creates methane gas which has to be drawn off

Can pollute the soil and groundwater underneath

Figure 18.1
Problems caused by a landfill site

Solutions to urban sprawl

Because urban sprawl brings many problems, Glasgow City Council has tried to reduce it.

1. **A Green Belt has been set up. This is a zone around the city in which no development can take place.** It stops the city growing outwards and prevents problems such as the loss of farmland and wildlife. Glasgow has had a Green Belt since the 1950s. This has reduced urban sprawl but it has **led to more building taking place beyond the Green Belt**. This has been especially in villages and small towns with good road and rail connections to the city. Places such as Bearsden and Bishopton have grown in size quickly. House prices there have gone up and the character of the settlement has changed. Another problem with Green Belts is that, although no urban development is allowed, exceptions have been made. New roads such as the M77 and the Southern Orbital pass through the Green Belt, and Cathkin landfill site and the Greenlaw development are also within it.
The Glasgow built-up area needs an extra 18,000 more housing units over the next few years and there is no space to build them all inside the city. Some will have to be built at the city edge.

2. As well as stopping development at the city edge, Glasgow also encourages development at brownfield sites inside the city. A *brownfield site* is a derelict site which can be built on again. Glasgow Council has developed several of these in its inner city, including the Old Docks and the Commonwealth Games Athletes' Village. By attracting housing, shops and businesses to the inner city, this should reduce developments at the city edge. However, brownfield sites are much more expensive to develop than greenfield sites. The remains of old buildings may have to be removed and sometimes the land is unstable or contaminated. So builders prefer to build at the city edge.

National 4

1. Describe the effects of urban sprawl on the countryside.
2. Describe the problems caused by new shopping centres in the suburbs.
3. Describe the effects on traffic of building new business parks in the suburbs.
4. Explain how new housing in the suburbs often leads to other developments.
5. Explain why landfill sites cause conflicts with local people.
6. (a) What is a Green Belt?
   (b) Do you think Glasgow's Green Belt has been successful? Give reasons for your answer.
7. (a) What is a brownfield site?
   (b) Why does Glasgow City Council want more developments on brownfield sites?

National 5

1. Describe the effects of urban sprawl on the countryside.
2. Describe the effects of urban sprawl on the amount of traffic (a) locally and (b) in the centre of the city.
3. Explain how one development in the suburbs often leads to others.
4. Explain why landfill sites are built near the edge of cities.
5. Describe the different types of pollution caused by landfill sites.
6. What effects does a Green Belt have on developments (a) inside the Green Belt, (b) beyond the Green Belt and (c) inside the city?

Activities

Activity A

Imagine you are a city councillor and you decide whether planning applications are granted. You know that you should not allow new developments on the Green Belt. You know the problems that urban sprawl brings. But you also need to do what is best for the local people, the people who voted for you.

Three applications have been received to build on an area of the city's Green Belt. Read them all and decide whether any should go ahead. Give reasons for your decisions.

APPLICATION FOR A NEW BUSINESS PARK

Please allow this development at the edge of Glasgow. It will bring many benefits to the city:

- It will bring 550 jobs, mostly well-paid.
- It will be built in an area of high unemployment.
- The buildings will not produce any air, noise or water pollution.
- Two new roads will be built to reduce traffic on existing local roads.

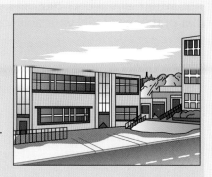

APPLICATION FOR A NEW RETAIL PARK

Please allow this development at the edge of Glasgow. It will bring many benefits to the city:

- It will bring 230 jobs which will be given to local people in order to reduce poverty levels in this part of the city.
- People will have more to spend so other businesses will prosper.
- We shall only build on poor-quality farmland.
- It will be landscaped to look attractive.

18

Activities continued...

APPLICATION FOR A NEW HOUSING ESTATE

Please allow this development at the edge of Glasgow. It will bring

- It will provide 178 new homes.
- 260 workers will be needed to build the houses.
- There will be houses for all income groups.
- A new lake will be created and wildlife will be encouraged.
- A new leisure centre will be built with cheap entry for all local people.

Activity B

A city urgently needs a new landfill site. Five sites are being considered. These are shown by the letters A–E in Figure 18.3. Which site do you think should be chosen? Give reasons for your decision.

Activity C

Would you like to live near a landfill site? If not, where should our rubbish be taken? What problems would your solution cause?

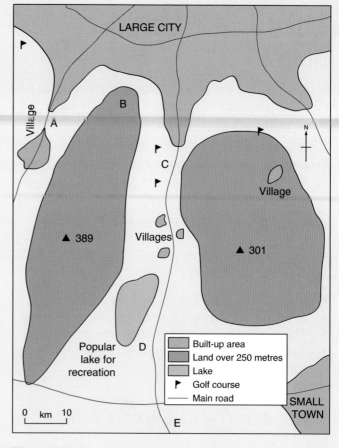

Figure 18.3
Possible locations for a landfill site

Now complete the 'I can do' boxes for this chapter.

Chapter 19

Case study of a developing city: Mumbai, India

By the end of this chapter, you should be able to:

✓ describe the site of Mumbai
✓ describe how Mumbai has grown over time
✓ give some of the reasons why it has grown.

Mumbai (which used to be called Bombay) is the largest city in India. It is a city of many contrasts, which is typical of a city in a developing country. It has the glamour of India's film industry, designer shops, exclusive apartments and 5-star hotels. It has reminders of the time when the British ruled India, with leafy cricket grounds and red double-decker buses. But it is also one of the most crowded cities in the world, with a population of over 20 million. It has acute and widespread poverty, the biggest slums in the whole of Asia and a large criminal underworld. Added to this is a mixture of different cultures, religions and ethnic groups.

Site

Mumbai's original site was an island off the west coast of India. It grew as a **fishing and trading port** and as a small industrial centre and then spread onto six more islands. The wetlands between these islands have now been reclaimed to form one island, Bombay Island.

Year	Population (approx.)
1650	10,000
1700	20,000
1750	70,000
1800	150,000
1850	800,000
1900	820,000
1950	3.0 million
1960	4.2 million
1970	6.0 million
1980	8.2 million
1990	12.5 million
2000	16.4 million
2010	19.9 million

Figure 19.1
Changes in Mumbai's population

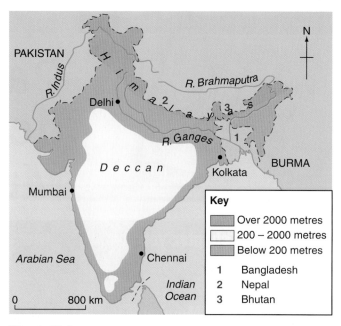

Figure 19.2
Location of Mumbai in India

Early growth

Mumbai started to grow when railways were built and factories began to appear. The first railways connected the cotton-growing areas inland with Mumbai, which led to the building of **cotton spinning and weaving mills**. By 1900, hundreds of thousands of people worked in this industry alone and there were many other industries, such as chemicals and engineering, which were attracted by the large labour force and excellent communications by rail and water.

Growth since independence

After India gained independence from Britain in 1947, Mumbai's manufacturing industries expanded but its service industries developed even faster. The **financial services** industry grew, with a lot more banks, finance houses and insurance companies setting up in what was now India's biggest and most prosperous city.

Meanwhile the **film industry**, which began 100 years ago, also expanded rapidly. Today, Mumbai has the biggest film industry in the world (called Bollywood), which turns out more films per year

Figure 19.3
Luxury apartments in Mumbai

than does Hollywood. The film industry relies on wealthy people to finance its productions and Mumbai has more wealthy people than any other Indian city. In addition, the varied scenery nearby and the dry, sunny weather for six months of the year make it very suitable for outdoor filming.

In the 1990s multi-national companies, such as IBM, British Airways and Prudential, began moving their **call centres** here because wage rates were much lower than in developed countries (as much as 90 per cent lower) and wages make up most of the operating costs of a call centre. There is also an educated workforce – wages are twice those earned by teachers here, so call centres attract many graduates, and productivity is higher than in developed countries.

Figure 19.4
A shanty town in Mumbai

As industry expanded, the city was able to improve its roads, port and airport. It could also afford to build new schools, universities and hospitals. With more and more wealthy people, entertainments increased and large shopping malls were constructed.

But in the countryside, life did not improve. It became increasingly difficult to make a living, the weather and harvests were unreliable, there were few services and people were aware of how much better life was in the city. An ever increasing number headed for Mumbai, the obvious choice of **centre for rural immigrants**.

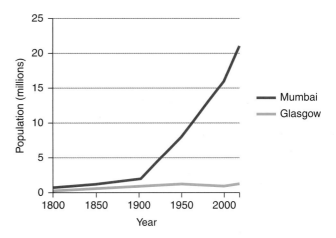

Figure 19.5
Populations of Glasgow and Mumbai

Mumbai today

Today **Mumbai is the industrial powerhouse of India**, as shown by Figure 19.6.

- Its port handles 40% of India's trade by sea.
- Its airport handles 60% of India's trade by air.
- It provides 10% of all the factory jobs in India.
- Its factories make 25% of all the goods that are made in India, by value.
- Its people pay 33% of all the income tax raised.

Figure 19.6
The importance of Mumbai

These are the reasons why the city's population has shot up and is now approaching 20 million.

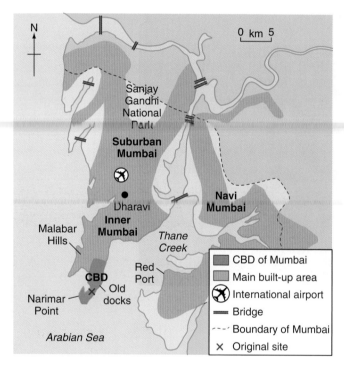

Figure 19.7
Mumbai: site and built-up areas

Land uses

As Mumbai grew, the original site was taken over by businesses and this became the city's CBD. As the city has continued to grow, so has the CBD, westwards and southwards to occupy most of south Mumbai (Figure 19.7). The main land uses here are similar to those found in the CBDs of other world cities. It has government buildings, hotels, entertainments and, especially, shops and offices.

The CBD also contains some old industrial areas, especially the old docks on the eastern side of the island. The remaining old industry is found next to the CBD and still in south Mumbai. Many of these old factories have now closed, especially the cotton mills.

Further out in the suburbs are newer industrial areas and technology parks and at the city edge to the east is Navi Mumbai (New Bombay). This has been built during the last 40 years and includes Mumbai's new port, many other new industries, as well as shopping centres and homes for over one million people.

Housing, for both rich and poor, is found all over the city, including in the CBD. Overall it takes up a far greater area than any other land use in Mumbai.

National 4

1. Using Figure 19.2, describe where Mumbai is located.
2. Why can Mumbai be described as a 'typical developing city'?
3. Using Figure 19.5, describe the main changes in Glasgow's population.
4. Using Figure 19.5, describe the main changes in Mumbai's population.
5. Describe the main differences shown in Figures 19.3 and 19.4.
6. Choose one of the main industries in Mumbai (past or present). Give two reasons why it set up here.
7. If you had to give just one reason why Mumbai has grown, what would it be? Explain your choice.
8. Look at Figure 19.7. Where is:
   (a) the original site of Mumbai?
   (b) the newest part of Mumbai?
9. Describe Mumbai's CBD.

National 5

1. Describe the site of Mumbai.
2. With the help of Figures 19.3 and 19.4, describe the differences in living standards within Mumbai.
3. Choose one of the main industries in Mumbai (past or present). Give two reasons why it set up here.
4. Do you think Mumbai has grown chiefly because of its employment opportunities, or because of the lack of employment opportunities in the countryside? Give reasons for your answer.
5. Using Figure 19.5, compare the growth of population in Glasgow and Mumbai.
6. Describe how Mumbai has grown outwards over the years.
7. In what ways is Mumbai's CBD similar to Glasgow's CBD?

Activities

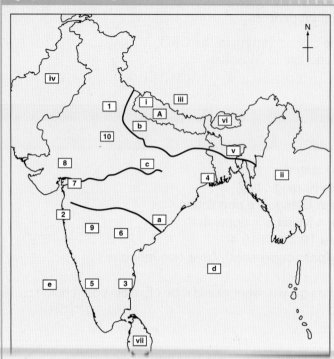

Figure 19.8
Physical features and cities of India

Study Figure 19.8. Using an atlas, answer the questions below:

1. Name the cities numbered 1 to 10.
2. Name the rivers a, b and c.
3. Name the seas d and e.
4. Name countries i to vii.
5. Name the mountain range A.

Now complete the 'I can do' boxes for this chapter.

Chapter 20

Housing problems in Mumbai

This chapter looks at housing problems in Mumbai.

By the end of this chapter, you should be able to:

✓ describe some features of squatter camps and shanty towns
✓ describe some of their problems
✓ give examples of solutions to the housing problems in Mumbai.

Did you know....? One billion people worldwide live in slums.

In the last fifteen years Mumbai's population has increased by the size of the whole population of Scotland. (Imagine the whole population of Scotland suddenly moving to Dundee!) How can it afford to build homes for an extra 5 million people? The short answer is, it can't.

The housing has to try and cater for the different tastes and incomes of the huge range of people who live in the city. So there are million-pound apartments for rich industrialists, large, stylish mansions for Bollywood film stars, tenement blocks for factory workers, shanty-town housing for the impoverished and squatter camps for destitute immigrants. More people live in squatter camps and shanty towns than in any other type of housing in Mumbai, and they are scattered all over the city (see Figure 20.1).

Squatter camps

The poorest accommodation in Mumbai is found in squatter areas. **Squatter areas are places where people settle on land which they do not own or rent**, and they build their own accommodation there. The **accommodation is nothing more than a basic, makeshift shelter**.

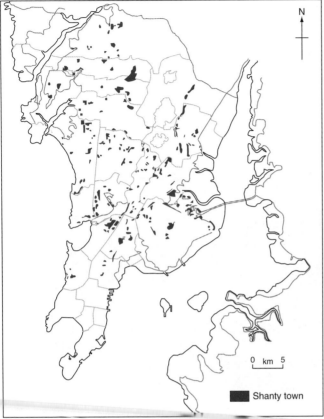

Figure 20.1
Shanty towns in Mumbai

Figure 20.2
A squatter camp at the edge of Mumbai

It is made of materials the people can find easily, usually cloth or plastic sheeting, supported by wooden poles. **It has no amenities** – that is, no toilet, no water, no kitchen, no bath, no electricity. Because squatter camps are illegal, **the authorities do not provide any services**, such as schools, health centres or rubbish collection. These conditions result in a high level of disease (malaria, cholera, dysentery, typhoid) from contact with contaminated water, flies and vermin. The children are often poorly educated and so find it difficult to obtain well-paid jobs and to escape from these areas.

Most of the people who come to live in squatter areas are new immigrants from rural areas, who have no money, no job and cannot afford even the cheapest accommodation in the city. **They set up either on the streets near the centre, as pavement dwellers, or at the edge of the city along main roads** where land is available. **The sites are often unsafe** – for example, in marshy areas that are prone to flooding and mosquitoes, on steep hillsides that suffer occasional mudslides, or very close to railway lines. There are literally hundreds of squatter areas in Mumbai (Figure 20.2).

Did you know…?
In 2011, 60% of people in Mumbai were living in slums.

Shanty towns

As long as they are not bulldozed, **squatter areas will grow until they are large enough to be called shanty towns**. Because they have been in existence for longer, **shanty towns have slightly better living conditions**, but overall conditions are still very poor. Shanty towns typically have the following characteristics:

- Houses may have brick walls and tin roofs, but many are still made of scrap materials.
- Houses are still very small and very overcrowded. Their average size is 9 metres square, and usually an extended family of between six and ten people lives there.
- Houses have no legal electricity, but may obtain it illegally.
- There may be access to a water supply in shanty towns, usually standpipes that many people share, and which work for only a couple of hours a day.
- There may be basic community toilets or latrines, but there are too few and they are badly maintained and unhygienic. In many areas, open gutters carry sewage away.
- Shanty towns may have roads, but they are not paved or signposted.
- There is no organised refuse collection and rubbish is dumped on any available space.
- There are no police, medical or fire fighting services. Fires are a major problem in shanty towns and they can spread very quickly.
- There are very few schools and few children are able to attend.
- There are high rates of crime, suicide, drug use and disease.
- Shanty towns are very overcrowded.
- Some shanty towns have developed small industries and workshops.

Figure 20.3
A shanty town in Mumbai

Solutions to the housing problems

Shanty towns and squatter areas give the Mumbai authorities many problems. **The living conditions are very poor, the crime rate is above average and disease is commonplace. They also present a bad image of the city.** Many are in unsafe areas. In July 2000, one shanty town on a steep slope collapsed and killed scores of people.

The Indian government has tried various methods in order to improve conditions in shanty towns and to reduce the problem of overcrowding in the city.

Thousands of **people were evicted** from their homes and their houses were bulldozed in an attempt to destroy shanty towns. However, this was not successful as people just built elsewhere in the city.

Another attempt by the government was to have people relocated to safer areas with basic amenities. They were **moved to high-rise buildings**, often in the suburbs. However, this proved unpopular because it meant people were further away from their work. They were also concerned that the government would not keep its promises.

An alternative plan is for the authorities to improve the shanty towns. They do this by **providing more toilets, standpipes and schools** and reinforcing the walls of houses. People could be given **legal rights to the land**. This might work but there are some shanty towns that are so overcrowded that it would be difficult to improve them, and it would still cost the authorities too much money.

Another method is for **residents to form co-operatives and organise improvements themselves**. They may be given the opportunity to design and plan these areas and have a say in what needs improving.

Because it cannot provide for all the people now living in Mumbai, **the city authority has built a new town** called Navi Mumbai (or New Bombay). It hopes that this will reduce the number of people living in Mumbai and so reduce pressure on housing in the city. Plans first took shape in the 1970s and building began on a large area of farmland north-east of the city, which contained nearly 100 villages. Over one million people now live here in twenty separate but connected settlements. It is intended that Navi Mumbai will have enough jobs and services for all the people living there, which will help to reduce Mumbai's problems.

National 4

1. What is (a) a squatter area and (b) a shanty town?
2. Describe five ways in which shanty towns are better than squatter areas.
3. Who is most likely to live in a squatter area?
4. What is the average size of a house in a shanty town? What is the average number of people who live in that house?
5. Why do few children attend schools in shanty towns?
6. Describe what you think it would be like to live in a shanty town.
7. Make a table in your jotter like the one below.

Solution	Success?

Using information from the text, complete your table to show the methods used by the Indian authorities to solve the problem of shanty towns, and suggest how successful the methods have been.

8. Which of the solutions do you think is the best in terms of solving Mumbai's housing problem? Give reasons for your answer.

National 5

1. What are the definitions of a squatter camp and a shanty town?
2. Describe, in detail, the differences between squatter areas and shanty towns.
3. Describe, in detail, the environmental quality in shanty towns and squatter areas.
4. Describe three solutions to shanty towns in Mumbai.
5. Which is the best solution? Give reasons for your answer.

Activities

Activity A

Using Figures 20.2 and 20.3, draw a poster describing the differences in housing in squatter areas and shanty towns.

Activity B

Read the statements below carefully and decide whether each statement is more likely to be describing a squatter camp or a shanty town.

Is a squatter camp or a shanty town more likely to …

1. have slightly better living conditions?
2. have very high levels of disease?
3. not have any rent to be paid?
4. have latrines?
5. not receive any public services?
6. consist of nothing more than a basic, makeshift shelter?
7. have no amenities?
8. be located on the streets near the centre or at the edge of the city along the main roads?
9. have roads?
10. house many immigrants?

Now complete the 'I can do' boxes for this chapter.

Chapter 21

Case study of a shanty town in Mumbai: Dharavi ①

By the end of this chapter, you should be able to:

✓ describe the growth of Dharavi
✓ describe some of the features of Dharavi
✓ describe some of the problems of Dharavi.

Did you know....?
With one million people, Dharavi is not even the largest shanty town in Mumbai.

There are literally hundreds of shanty towns in Mumbai but probably the most famous is Dharavi, because it featured in the film *Slumdog Millionaire* and also in some British TV programmes and Bollywood films. **It is near the centre of Mumbai**, next to the financial district, and occupies a small area of 175 hectares (less than one square mile) between two railway lines. In this very small area **live one million people** in extremely crowded conditions.

Growth

Dharavi was once a fishing village but the land around it was drained in the 1800s and this allowed more people to settle here. These were migrants from other parts of India, mainly potters, leather tanners and embroidery workers who used their skills to start workshops here. Dharavi has continued to attract people from the countryside who want to have a higher standard of living in the city or who have been forced to leave their farms. It grew steadily in the nineteenth century, quickly in the twentieth century, and very very quickly at the end of the twentieth century when people were moving here at a rate of 200 per day.

Features of Dharavi

- **Land use** Today, in this one small area of Mumbai live **one million people** in 85 distinct areas with different religions, cultures, social groups (castes) and languages. In addition, there are **15,000 one-room factories**, including 3500 garment workshops and 5000 leather workshops, as well as a large pottery district and recycling area. There are also **hundreds of small shops** where people can buy most of the things they need, and just as many which make and sell food.

- **Ownership** The local government owns the land in Dharavi but the residents do not pay them rent, which makes them **illegal squatters**. They do **pay rent**, but it is to a local landlord who looks after their area of Dharavi.

- **Building materials** The newest part is around the edge where **flimsy housing is built by recent arrivals using scrap material** from nearby – wood, cloth and corrugated iron. A maze of passageways leads into the heart of Dharavi where the **oldest and most solid buildings** are found. These have been improved over the years and are now **made of brick and concrete**.

- **Houses** Most houses began as one room but have been added to over the years. Older ones may have another floor and a separate kitchen area. **The average size is 3 metres × 3 metres** (pace it) and the average extended family size is between six and ten people.

- **Water** Water comes from **standpipes** but is only available for a couple of hours each day.

- **Toilets (sewerage)** There is one toilet for approximately 500 people but these are often blocked. **Most people just use the shallow river** as a toilet.

- **Electricity** Most houses have electricity but it is irregular and unreliable. It is also **illegal**, having been 'tapped' from the city's power lines.

- **Employment** Almost everyone works – they have to in order to survive. There is no unemployment or sickness benefit. Eighty per cent of people work in Dharavi, in its many workshops and small factories. In many buildings, the ground floor is the workshop and the family or workers live upstairs.

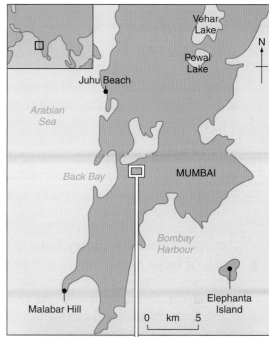

Figure 21.1
Location of Dharavi
Imagery ©2013 Cnes/Spot Image, DigitalGlobe, Map data ©2013 Google

Figure 21.2
A passageway in Dharavi

Problems

- **It is unhealthy** The biggest problem is the poor sanitation with raw sewage flowing between rows of shacks and with children often playing in it. The pipes that bring the water are sometimes cracked and sewage seeps in. This pollutes the water supply and is the main cause of ill-health. The nearest hospital receives 3000 cases per day of people from Dharavi with **diarrhoea and diseases such as typhoid**. Tuberculosis, malaria and diphtheria are also very common, as is malnutrition. In addition, people often work in dangerous conditions with toxic substances and they are crowded together, so disease spreads very quickly. As a result **life expectancy here is only 50 years**.

- **Lack of basic services** Apart from there being very few toilets and safe water, there is **no rubbish collection**. There are many rats and flies which can also spread disease. Until recently the local authorities did not provide any social services as the people were living here illegally, but in the last 50 years, 60 primary schools, four secondary schools and one state hospital have been built. There are still **far too few state schools and hospitals** and instead most people use private schools and health centres. People have to pay for these which inevitably means that many children do not go to school, **literacy rates are low** and so is life expectancy. One of the residents' biggest worries is not being able to afford the medicines that their families need.

- **No taxes are paid** The government and local government lose out because no one pays them rent for the land they own. Worse still, few people and few factory and workshop owners pay tax to the government. This is called **the informal economy** – it is outside the proper laws. Among other things this means there is no protection against factories releasing dangerous toxic materials or employing children. It also means Mumbai has much less money to spend improving the city.

- **Poor image** Some people say that this overcrowded, illegal, noisy area, made of rough shacks and smelling of sewage, is an eyesore, which puts off tourists from visiting the city and big companies from setting up here. This might be true, but there is a different view of Dharavi, as is explained in the next chapter.

Did you know....?
People who live in shanty towns are the biggest builders of houses in the world.

National 4

1. Where is Dharavi located?
2. (a) Why did Dharavi grow?
   (b) How quickly did it grow?
3. Apart from housing, what else is found in Dharavi?
4. Decide whether each of these statements about Dharavi is **true** or **false**.
   (a) The local Mumbai authority owns the land in Dharavi.
   (b) People pay rent to the local authority.
   (c) All the housing is flimsy.
   (d) The average house is about the same size as a classroom.
   (e) Most houses have a toilet and a cold water tap.
   (f) People have to pay for electricity.
   (g) Most people have a long journey to work each day.
5. Look at all the features of Dharavi. Which would you find most difficult to tolerate and why?
6. Explain why it is unhealthy in Dharavi.
7. Why are there so few services, such as schools and hospitals?
8. There is an informal economy in Dharavi, in which people do not obey some government laws. Name two things people do in Dharavi that are against the law.

National 5

1. Describe the location of Dharavi.
2. Describe the growth of Dharavi's population.
3. Describe the variety of housing found in Dharavi.
4. Describe the types of jobs available in Dharavi.
5. Look at all the features of Dharavi. Which would you find most difficult to tolerate, and why?
6. Life expectancy here is fifteen years less than in the rest of India. In detail, explain why.
7. Explain why literacy rates are also very low.
8. (a) What is meant by 'the informal economy'?
   (b) Describe one advantage and one disadvantage of the informal economy to a resident of Dharavi.
9. What everyday activities in Dharavi are illegal?

Activities

Activity A

Look at the problems of Dharavi. Which, do you think, is the worst problem in the eyes of:

- a teenage resident of Mumbai
- a 45-year-old who has lived in Dharavi for his whole life
- the Mumbai authorities
- an international charity such as Oxfam?

Give reasons for your answers.

Activities continued...

Activity B

Try and work out the most likely explanation for these true statements:

Officials admit they do not know the population of Dharavi

Self-made millionaires living in Dharavi!

Figure 21.3

Now complete the 'I can do' boxes for this chapter.

Chapter

22

Case study of a shanty town in Mumbai: Dharavi ②

This chapter looks at developments in the shanty town of Dharavi.

By the end of this chapter, you should be able to:

✓ describe some of the benefits of Dharavi
✓ describe some features of the Dharavi Redevelopment Project
✓ describe some features of a self-improvement plan for Dharavi.

It is true that Dharavi is an overcrowded, illegal, noisy area, made of rough shacks and smelling of sewage, but that is not the whole story. Just ask the residents: the vast majority do not want to leave. So what benefits does Dharavi bring?

Figure 22.1
A workshop in Dharavi

Benefits

- **It provides cheap, affordable housing** Mumbai cannot build enough houses for all its people. Renting accommodation elsewhere in the city is expensive. Rents in Dharavi can be as little as £3 per month, so even the poorest can live here.
- **It provides a lot of employment** There are thousands of small workshops and factories here which pay low wages but which together give employment to most of the residents. Many skilled people work here and pass on their skills to others, for example metalsmiths, garment workers and potters. Now there is even a small tourist industry, with guided tours of the shanty town.
- **It brings the city a lot of money** Some of Dharavi's goods are exported all over the world – the total value of everything made here in a year is over £300 million. Much of this money is spent in Mumbai. The recycling industry here is vast, and 80 per cent of all Mumbai's waste is recycled (compare this with 23 per cent in the UK).
- **Very low crime rate** Conditions are overcrowded, most houses do not even have doors and certainly no locks, but crime rates are lower here than in the rest of the city.
- **It is very sociable** There are communal open areas where people can sit and chat, and many of the daily chores, such as washing and repairing clothes, are done together. The feeling of belonging to a community is very strong.
- **People work very hard and are very enterprising** – they pass on these attitudes to the next generation, which must benefit the city.

Changes

Dharavi Redevelopment Project

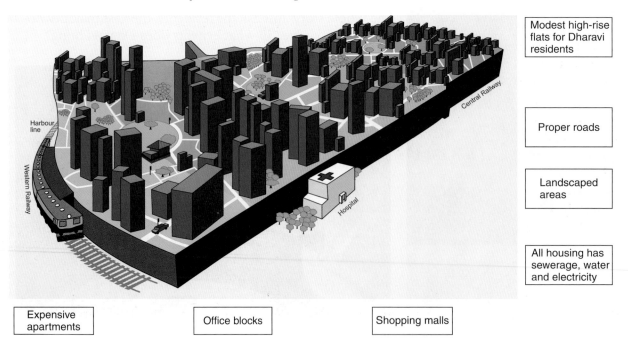

Modest high-rise flats for Dharavi residents

Proper roads

Landscaped areas

All housing has sewerage, water and electricity

Expensive apartments

Office blocks

Shopping malls

Figure 22.2
Architect's plan for the Dharavi Redevelopment Project

Many people, including the Mumbai authorities, think the problems of Dharavi outweigh its benefits and that the area should be redeveloped. To make this possible, in 2004 the Dharavi Redevelopment Project was drawn up. It was expected to be completed by 2013 but in fact it had not even started in that year, although the plans have been approved by the Mumbai authorities.

Some features of the project:

- Part of Dharavi will have to be knocked down.
- This is where at least 57,000 families live.
- High-rise apartments will be built for some residents.
- Each family will receive a 21-square metre apartment.
- The apartments will have water, sewerage and electricity.
- Only residents who have lived in Dharavi since before the year 2000 will be eligible for an apartment.
- Other residents will be rehoused elsewhere in the city.
- Only industries that do not cause pollution will be able to relocate here.
- This leaves about half the area for building expensive houses, offices and malls.
- The project will take seven years to build and will cost £2 billion.
- It will be paid for by private companies, not by the city of Mumbai.

The main drawbacks are:

- **Only some families will be rehoused in Dharavi**, which is where the vast majority want to live.
- People are unhappy that they will be given such **small apartments**. Although the new apartments will have more floorspace, in the shanty town residents have made an extra storey in many of their houses, which will not be possible in the new apartments.
- Many families are currently **living above their workshops** which **would be very difficult** in high-rise apartments.
- People are concerned that **many of the workshops** that give off pollution, such as metalworking, **will be banned** with the new laws.
- There is **not enough space being given to industries such as pottery and recycling** – these employ many people and bring in a lot of money, but they need large areas of land. If there is no recycling, there will be a lot of waste and litter all over the city.

Because of these drawbacks, some people argue that the Dharavi Redevelopment Project does not help Dharavi residents much. The people to benefit most from this scheme are the well-off residents of Mumbai who will now have new luxury apartments and malls. Major companies will also have brand new offices next to the financial district.

Self-improvement plan

There is no other plan on the table for Dharavi but evidence from around the world suggests that the most successful housing schemes must involve the

Figure 22.3
Mahila Milan, a self-help women's group in Dharavi

residents. **These are called self-help schemes**. An alternative self-improvement plan for Dharavi would involve the following:

- First the residents form separate self-help groups in different areas of Dharavi.
- One group of residents persuades the authorities to give them ownership of their land.
- Then they can design their own improvements. These include:
  - building many more toilets, which would be properly maintained
  - improving the water supply
  - building another floor onto their houses
  - making stronger walls.
- The people of Dharavi have a huge range of skills and can form self-help groups to carry out many of these improvements.
- Some self-help groups will negotiate small loans from banks.
- Others will negotiate with the authorities to provide them with some basic services, such as legal electricity and piped water.

Such a self-improvement plan:

- costs much less money because the people do much of the work themselves
- means that everyone can stay in Dharavi
- allows the thousands of businesses to continue
- brings the improvements the residents most want
- brings the community together because they need to discuss and agree on improvements.

There are extraordinary difficulties involved in trying to improve conditions in such an overcrowded area as Dharavi – far more difficult than any local council in the UK has had to face. And Dharavi is just one of many shanty towns in Mumbai. What is very clear is that the Mumbai authorities do not have the money to improve these areas themselves. Do they give the residents some help and let them do the rest, or do they enlist the help and huge resources of all the wealthy people and companies in Mumbai and the rest of India?

National 4

1. Describe two of the benefits of Dharavi.
2. In what ways is Dharavi better than the area where you live?
3. What is the biggest benefit of Dharavi, in your opinion? Give reasons for your answer.
4. Look again at the problems of Dharavi in the previous chapter. Do you think its problems outweigh its benefits, or not? Justify your answer.
5. List:
   (a) three facts about the Dharavi Redevelopment Project
   (b) three benefits it will bring
   (c) three reasons why some people dislike the project.
6. The alternative plan for Dharavi involves setting up self-help groups of residents. List four different types of self-help group that would make improvements.
7. Which do you think is a better plan for Dharavi: the self-improvement plan or the redevelopment project? Give your reasons.

National 5

1. Explain convincingly why Dharavi is such an asset to Mumbai.
2. In what ways is Dharavi better than the area where you live?
3. Look again at the problems of Dharavi described in the previous chapter. Do you think its problems outweigh its benefits, or not? Justify your answer.
4. Describe the main features of the Dharavi Redevelopment Project.
5. Draw a table with two columns and list the benefits and drawbacks of this scheme.
6. (a) What are self-help groups?
   (b) What improvements would they make possible in Dharavi?
7. Draw another table with two columns and list the benefits and drawbacks of a self-improvement plan.

Activities

The people of Dharavi are very enterprising and resourceful in starting up guided tours of Dharavi. *You* are now that enterprising person! You must come up with a business plan.

1. First you need to answer these questions:
   - Where will you take the tourists, how long will the tour take, and how will you travel around? Remember: This is Dharavi!
   - What do you think will be your *demographic* – what nationalities, gender and age range will your tourists be?
   - What costs will you have?
   - How much will you charge?
   - How many people can you take during one day?
   - How much profit will you make each day and in a year?
   - What name will you give your company?
   - Where will you advertise your tour?
2. Now design an advertisement for your tour.
3. What will you say during your tour? Write 100 words to give an idea of the theme and purpose of your tour. Remember: You and your family have lived here all your lives.
4. Next, write this up as a proper business plan, with the title: 'Business Plan for a Tour Company of Dharavi'. You need to include all these elements:
   - The name of your company
   - The theme and purpose of the tour
   - A description of the tour route
   - Your market – who will be your customers and how/where you will advertise
   - Your costs
   - Your income
   - Your profit

Now complete the 'I can do' boxes for this chapter.

Chapter 23

This chapter looks at farming in the Great Plains, USA.

The rural landscape in a developed country: the Great Plains, USA

By the end of this chapter, you should be able to:

✓ describe the location and physical landscape of the Great Plains
✓ describe the land use pattern in the Great Plains
✓ describe the main characteristics of extensive commercial farming here.

Location

The Great Plains is one of the major farming areas in the world. **It is a huge area of flat land** running down the **middle of the USA** and extending from northern Mexico into Canada. In total it is 3200 km from north to south and 800 km from west to east.

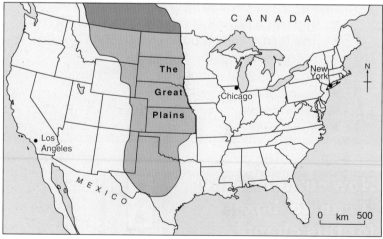

Figure 23.1
Location of the Great Plains

Climate

Due to its huge area, wide variations in climate are experienced in the Great Plains, from north to south and from east to west. These variations are shown in Figures 23.5 and 23.6.

The **northern states are typically much cooler** with very cold and snowy winters and mild summers, while the **southern states can be hot all year round**. **The western states are semi-arid** with hot summers and mild winters. In these states, drought is very common, and they can experience devastating dust storms. The **eastern states are considerably wetter** and the rainfall is more reliable.

The physical landscape

The land in the Great Plains is vast and undulating. Most is very flat but occasionally the horizon is broken up by hills such as the Black Hills of Dakota.

The semi-arid and arid climate creates many problems in some of the states in the Great Plains, such as Kansas and Texas. The prolonged periods without rain can lead to **drought conditions**. (A *drought* is a long period without rain.) During this time, the vegetation dies as there is no water to sustain it. With little or no vegetation cover the soil dries up and is easily blown away. Then the land becomes infertile.

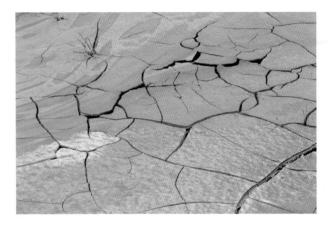

Figure 23.2
The effects of drought and soil erosion

One further problem created by drought and **soil erosion** is **dust storms**. The dry soil turns to dust and is blown away by the strong winds. Dust storms were so frequent during the 1930s that the area became known as The Dust Bowl. At one point during the 1930s, an estimated half a million hectares of topsoil were blown away.

Figure 23.3
Dust storm in the Great Plains in the 1930s

Land use

Only 200 years ago this region was home to Native Americans who grew some crops but relied mostly on hunting bison. Then immigrant settlers from Europe set up cattle ranches here and drove away the Native Americans and their herds of bison. Just over a hundred years ago crop farmers took over much of the area and the population began to grow. By the early twentieth century the population was greater than it is now.

Then a series of droughts, together with poor farming practices, led to massive soil erosion and acute dust storms. Many people left the region as farming became impossible and living here became intolerable. This rural depopulation allowed the remaining farms to increase in size and by the late twentieth century **farms had become extremely large**.

The **population of the Great Plains remains very low** today. Seventy per cent of the land is used for farming but the vast **majority of people live in urban areas** with only 33 per cent living in the countryside. Because the population is so low and the farms so big, settlements are dispersed. The villages and towns tend to be evenly distributed, with the largest settlements found where main roads meet.

> **Did you know....?**
> In 2007, the total population of the Great Plains was 9.9 million – that is just 3% of the USA's population.

> **Did you know....?**
> Settlements in the Great Plains were originally 16 km apart. This was the furthest distance that could be reached there and back in one day by horse and cart.

Farming

This region is a major farming area. It produces nearly two-thirds of the nation's wheat, more than half its beef, a fifth of its corn, a quarter of its cotton, four-fifths of its grain sorghum and a sixth of its pork.

Differences in farming can be seen across the region. **Vast cattle ranches dominate the western states**, while **huge arable farms in the east** grow mainly wheat, cotton, barley, hay and corn (Figure 23.4).

All **farming here is extensive and commercial** – *extensive* because of the huge area of land covered by each farm. The average farm in the Great Plains is 400 hectares – that is the equivalent of 400 football pitches – but they can be much bigger in the drier west. *Commercial farming* means growing crops or rearing animals to make money. All of the crops that are grown or animals that are reared will be sold so the farmer can earn a living.

The **farms in the Great Plains are large because**:

- **soils are quite infertile** as they contain little humus – this means the farmer needs a large area to produce a profit
- **land is cheap** – as more and more people left the region, fewer people wanted to buy farms here and so the price of land dropped.

But huge farms are only possible today because of the **great variety of machinery** that is used. The flat land is well-suited to machines and machines are much cheaper to use than workers.

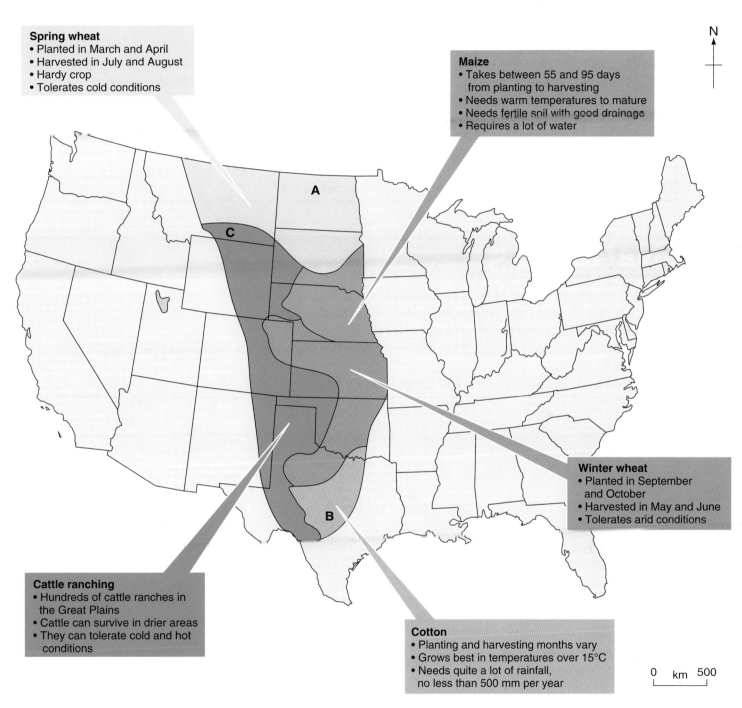

Spring wheat
• Planted in March and April
• Harvested in July and August
• Hardy crop
• Tolerates cold conditions

Maize
• Takes between 55 and 95 days from planting to harvesting
• Needs warm temperatures to mature
• Needs fertile soil with good drainage
• Requires a lot of water

N

Winter wheat
• Planted in September and October
• Harvested in May and June
• Tolerates arid conditions

Cattle ranching
• Hundreds of cattle ranches in the Great Plains
• Cattle can survive in drier areas
• They can tolerate cold and hot conditions

Cotton
• Planting and harvesting months vary
• Grows best in temperatures over 15°C
• Needs quite a lot of rainfall, no less than 500 mm per year

0   km   500

Figure 23.4
Types of farming in the Great Plains

National 4

1. Describe the location of the Great Plains.
2. Why does the climate vary so much in the Great Plains?
3. Describe the different climates in the Great Plains.
4. What does the term *drought* mean and why would this cause problems for farming?
5. What is the most common land use in the Great Plains?
6. Why have farms increased in size since the mid twentieth century?
7. Where are the largest settlements found?
8. What two types of farming take place in the Great Plains and where is each found?
9. Explain what extensive commercial farming is.
10. Why is so much farm machinery used in the Great Plains?

National 5

1. Describe the location of the Great Plains.
2. Describe, in detail, the different climates of the Great Plains.
3. Explain, in detail, the problems caused by the climate.
4. In your opinion, why do you think the majority of the population of the Great Plains live in urban areas?
5. Describe, in detail, farming in the Great Plains.

Activities

Activity A

1. Using an atlas and Figure 23.1, name:
   (a) the two most northerly US states in the Great Plains
   (b) the two most southerly states in the Great Plains
   (c) two central states in the Great Plains.
2. Using an atlas and Figure 23.4, name:
   (a) three states where spring wheat is the main crop
   (b) two states where maize is grown
   (c) three states growing winter wheat
   (d) three states rearing cattle
   (e) one state growing cotton.

Activity B

1. (a) Look at the location of A in Figure 23.4. At that place, what is the:
      (i) farming type, (ii) winter temperature (Figure 23.5), (iii) summer temperature (Figure 23.5), (iv) annual rainfall (Figure 23.6)?
   (b) Use the information above to try and explain why this type of farming is important at A.

Activities continued...

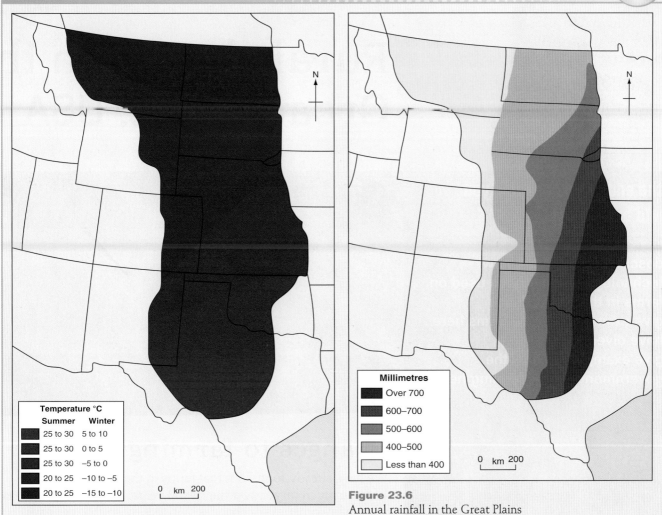

Temperature °C

Summer	Winter
25 to 30	5 to 10
25 to 30	0 to 5
25 to 30	−5 to 0
20 to 25	−10 to −5
20 to 25	−15 to −10

0   km   200

Figure 23.5
Temperatures in the Great Plains

Millimetres

■	Over 700
■	600–700
■	500–600
■	400–500
□	Less than 400

0   km   200

Figure 23.6
Annual rainfall in the Great Plains

2. (a) Look at the location of B in Figure 23.4. At that place, what is the:
   (i) farming type, (ii) winter temperature (Figure 23.5), (iii) summer temperature (Figure 23.5),
   (iv) annual rainfall (Figure 23.6)?
   (b) Use the information above to try and explain why this type of farming is important at B.
3. (a) Look at the location of C in Figure 23.4. At that place, what is the:
   (i) farming type, (ii) winter temperature (Figure 23.5), (iii) summer temperature (Figure 23.5),
   (iv) annual rainfall (Figure 23.6)?
   (b) Use the information above to try and explain why this type of farming is important at C.

Now complete the
'I can do' boxes
for this chapter.

Chapter

This chapter looks at recent changes in farming in the Great Plains, USA.

Rural change in the Great Plains, USA (1)

By the end of this chapter, you should be able to:

✓ describe some of the new technology and methods used on farms in the Great Plains
✓ give examples of how farms have diversified
✓ give examples of how the government affects farming here.

Changes to farming

We have already found out that farms in the Great Plains have become much bigger over the last 50 years, but farming here has seen many other major changes. Most of these changes have been an attempt to overcome the climate problems in the region.

Figure 24.1
Arable farming in the Great Plains

Change in farming	Reason	Example
Increased farm size	• More and more people left the Great Plains • Land was bought by remaining farmers in an attempt to increase output	All states in the Great Plains, such as North Dakota
Use of new technology For example: • Precision farming – use of satellite navigation to irrigate and apply chemicals precisely • Laser levelling of the land	• More efficient – saves money and water • Reduces soil erosion	Kansas, Texas
Improved farming methods For example: • Contour ploughing • Strip cultivation • Intercropping • Irrigation	• To try and reduce soil erosion which devastated the region in the 1930s and still causes problems	The Dust Bowl area of Oklahoma
More animals are now being kept	• Frequent droughts make crop growing unreliable • With more animals, more grass is grown which stops soil erosion	North Dakota
Different types of crops being grown For example: • Sunflowers • Millet	• Farmers are now growing crops that are better suited to dry conditions	Kansas ('the Sunflower state')
More money from the government For example: • The Conservation Reserve Program (farmers paid to take land out of crop production)	• To ensure higher standard of living for farmers • To ensure the country produces enough food • To protect soil and the environment	Texas
Growing more biofuels	• Farmers are given government help to grow biofuels (biofuels are discussed in Chapter 25)	All areas but especially the eastern states of the Great Plains
Diversification (other ways of making money than from traditional farming) For example: • Providing accommodation for tourists • Bison ranching	• More profitable • Farmers can make money from land taken out of crop production	Montana, Wyoming

National 4

1. Give examples of new technology on Great Plains farms and explain how it helps farmers.
2. Explain how the government affects what farmers do.
3. What is *farm diversification*?
4. Why do farmers use different methods now?
5. Which of the recent changes do you think has helped farmers most? Give reasons.

National 5

1. What effect has new technology had on farming in the Great Plains?
2. Describe and explain the different ways in which the government affects farming in the Great Plains.
3. Describe the ways in which farmers have tried to reduce soil erosion.
4. Explain why farms have diversified.
5. Which two changes have affected farmers most, do you think? Give reasons for your answer.

Activities

Should Farmer Joe concentrate on farming bison?

In pairs, or as a group, you need to decide whether or not Farmer Joe should stop farming crops in favour of farming bison.

You will need to do the following:

1. Carefully study the map in Figure 24.2.
2. Carefully read through all the statements in the boxes.
3. Sort all the information in a way that will help you decide what Farmer Joe should do. (There is no right or wrong answer – it is your decision.)
4. Based on all the information, feedback your decision to the class or teacher and explain it.

Activities continued...

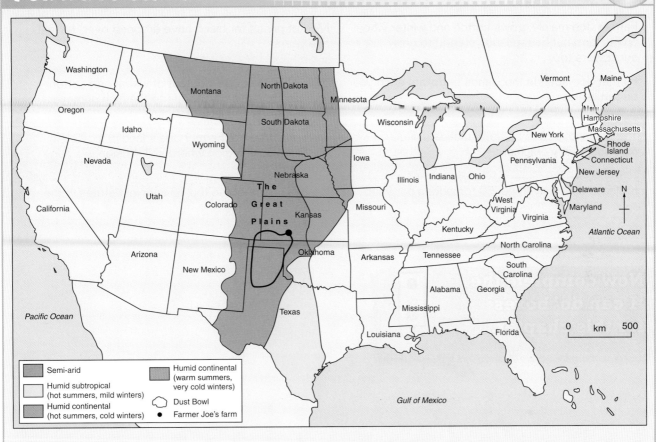

Figure 24.2
Farmer Joe's farm in the Great Plains

Farmer Joe owns an arable farm in Kansas.	Dust storms are a major problem in Kansas.
Kansas is prone to severe weather.	The soil on the farm is poor quality.
Farmer Joe has owned his farm since 1979.	Although it is a mainly arable farm, Farmer Joe also has a herd of 200 bison.
Kansas is a large state in the Great Plains.	Bison can be expensive – Farmer Joe needs to pay for animal feed and veterinary help.
The farm has been in Farmer Joe's family since the early 1900s.	Last year, Farmer Joe lost 10% of his bison herd due to an unexpected bovine disease.
Drought is a major problem in Kansas.	Winter wheat prices fluctuate annually.
Farmer Joe's farm is 375 hectares.	A bison's thick fur can offer great protection against the harsh elements.
Farmer Joe has spent thousands of dollars installing an irrigation system on his farm.	Cotton prices are at an all-time high.
Farmers receive financial help for diversifying into bison farming.	Bison meat contains less cholesterol and more protein than beef.

Activities continued...

Farmer Joe mainly grows cotton and winter wheat on his farm but has recently started to grow sunflowers too.	Market prices for bison have dropped over the last five years.
Farmer Joe spends thousands of dollars each year on fertilisers.	37% of Farmer Joe's output of wheat and cotton was destroyed last year due to the high summer temperatures and lack of rainfall.
The flat land around the farm makes using machinery very efficient.	A small portion of Farmer Joe's land is located in the Dust Bowl region where soil erosion is a huge problem.
Kansas has, on average, 50 tornadoes per year.	Kansas is one of the top 10 sunniest states in the USA.

Now complete the 'I can do' boxes for this chapter.

Chapter 25

Rural change in the Great Plains, USA (2)

This chapter looks at more farming changes in the Great Plains, USA.

By the end of this chapter, you should be able to:

✓ describe the reasons for and against growing biofuels in the Great Plains
✓ give reasons to support and oppose the use of genetically modified crops
✓ describe some of the reasons why farmers grow organic produce.

There have been many changes in the Great Plains over recent years but some of the more controversial changes include growing biofuels, using genetically modified crops and organic farming.

Biofuels

Figure 25.1
Growing biofuels in the Great Plains

Biofuels are seen as an environmentally friendly alternative to petrol and diesel. They are made from living matter such as corn, sugarcane and rapeseed. The crops that are grown are fermented to produce ethanol. Worldwide, more and more modern vehicles are being designed to run on ethanol and biodiesel. In the Great Plains corn and soybeans are two of the main crops grown to produce biofuels.

The US government set up the Renewable Fuel Standard programme in 2005 to ensure that the country produces its own biofuel. It sets minimum targets each year. For instance, in 2012 it insisted that 13 billion gallons (59 billion litres) of biofuel had to be produced in the USA and that 40 per cent of all the corn grown must be used in biofuel production. But, as biofuel crops become more common, people are also aware that they bring problems as well as benefits.

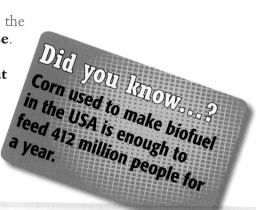

The problems with growing biofuel crops in the Great Plains are:

- The increased demand for corn (and other biofuel crops) causes the **price of biofuel crops, and consequently food, to increase**.
- Corn is used to feed livestock so this is increasing the costs of livestock farmers and as a result **increasing the price of meat and dairy products**.
- Corn has a very high water requirement, water supply in the Great Plains is already limited and so **scarce water is being used up quickly**.
- Biofuel crops need a lot of fertiliser to grow well, particularly in the Great Plains where growing conditions are not always suitable. Therefore, farmers use more chemicals which has **damaging effects on the environment**, particularly on water sources.

The UN has called for the USA to suspend its production of ethanol because **it is believed to be leading to a food crisis around the world**.

The advantages of growing biofuel crops in the Great Plains are:

- Producing more of its own fuel, rather than importing it, **saves the USA a lot of money**.
- **Thousands of jobs have been created** in the biofuel industry, reducing unemployment rates.
- **Billions of dollars are made** from the biofuel industries each year. In North Dakota alone, $300 million is made from the production of ethanol.
- **Farmers in the Great Plains have greatly benefited** from the biofuels industry. Farming went from being unproductive in many states to being very profitable.
- **When burned, biofuels emit less pollution** than fossil fuels, which should **reduce global warming**. The number of vehicles run on ethanol in the USA has been increasing steadily each year and so benefiting the environment.

Genetically modified crops

Genetically modified (GM) crops are plants that have been genetically altered by scientists so that they will grow better. (The plants have had genes from other plants put into them.)

Figure 25.2
A field of genetically modified crops

The use of GM crops in the USA is a controversial issue. Some argue that GM crops are a danger to people's health, while others feel that they are hugely beneficial to the economy.

Advantages	Disadvantages
Crops are being modified so that **they can tolerate drought**. In the Great Plains long summer droughts in many states can ruin crops for an entire growing season. Growing GM crops would ensure that yields are reliable each year.	One of the biggest arguments against using GM crops concerns people's health. Many scientists believe that altering crops from their natural state **could pose significant problems to people's health**.
In some of the northern states of the Great Plains, such as North Dakota, low temperatures and spring freezes can lead to crop failure. GM crops have now been altered so that **they can withstand low temperatures** and can grow regardless of how hot or cold it is.	There are concerns about the cost of GM crops. Some believe that **GM crops could be too expensive for many farmers** and therefore the wealth gap between rich and poor farmers will widen.
Farmers have many problems to contend with when growing crops. Disease caused by fungi and bacteria can ruin crops. GM crops have been designed to **resist diseases**, therefore reassuring farmers that their crops will be successful.	New types of crops entering the food chain **could be very damaging to other organisms** such as caterpillars.
Many crops are lost each year due to insect pests; this can lead to huge financial loss for the farmer. Farmers can use pesticides to try to minimise this problem but many consumers are put off eating crops treated in this way. GM crops can be engineered so that **they are resistant to pests**.	Scientist are worried that **insects may become resistant to GM crops**.
Due to the difficult climate in the Great Plains, there have been very few varieties of crops grown. Crops that have never been able to grow in regions before are now being grown at **huge financial gain for the farmer**.	

Figure 25.3
Advantages and disadvantages of GM crops

Organic farming

Organic farming can be both arable and livestock. Organic arable farmers do not use synthetic (artificial) pesticides and fertilisers to help them grow crops, and livestock farmers do not use growth hormones and antibiotics.

Organic farming in the Great Plains has seen a massive increase in recent years as demand for organic produce free from chemicals has soared. There are many arguments for and against organic farming.

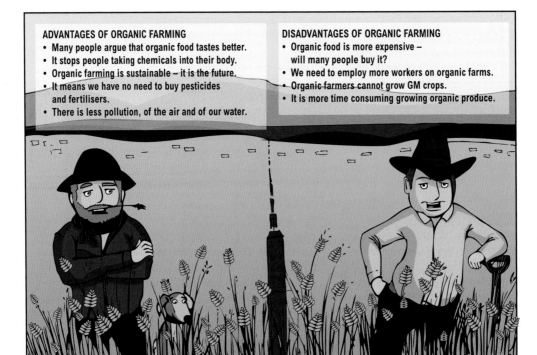

ADVANTAGES OF ORGANIC FARMING
- Many people argue that organic food tastes better.
- It stops people taking chemicals into their body.
- Organic farming is sustainable – it is the future.
- It means we have no need to buy pesticides and fertilisers.
- There is less pollution, of the air and of our water.

DISADVANTAGES OF ORGANIC FARMING
- Organic food is more expensive – will many people buy it?
- We need to employ more workers on organic farms.
- Organic farmers cannot grow GM crops.
- It is more time consuming growing organic produce.

Figure 25.4
Advantages and disadvantages of organic farming

National 4

1. What are three of the most controversial changes taking place in the Great Plains?
2. What are biofuels? What are they used for?
3. Are you for or against using biofuels? Give reasons why.
4. What are genetically modified crops?
5. (a) What are the main advantages of growing GM crops?
   (b) What are the main problems of growing GM crops?
6. If crops are grown organically, what does this mean?
7. If you were a farmer, do you think you would be an organic or a conventional farmer? Give reasons for your choice.

National 5

1. What are biofuels? What are they used for?
2. (a) What are the three main arguments for growing biofuels in the Great Plains?
   (b) What are the three main arguments against growing biofuels in the Great Plains?
3. What are genetically modified crops?
4. Do you support the use of GM crops? Give reasons for your answer.
5. If crops are grown organically, what does this mean?
6. If you were a farmer, do you think you would be an organic or a conventional farmer? Give reasons for you choice.

Activities

Read the following people's viewpoints on the three changes affecting farming in the Great Plains. In each case choose one view that you support and one view that you disagree with. Explain your choices.

Biofuels

> *My family have farmed this land for over one hundred years. With the difficult climate here it is impossible to make a decent profit selling our crops. Growing biofuels has been our saving grace.*

Biofuels farmer in the Great Plains

> *The number of vehicles on the roads in the USA has never been higher. We have the second largest number of vehicles per person in the world, with 812 vehicles per 1000 people. Most of these vehicles are being run on petrol and diesel, which are devastating to our climate and one of the biggest contributors to global warming. Biofuels will help reduce this by running cars on ethanol.*

Environmentalist

> *I rely on arable farmers in the Great Plains to produce feed for my animals. I have over 700 bison on my farm and they are very expensive to feed. With the increased cost of corn due to biofuel production, I struggle to pay for animal feed each year.*

Bison farmer in the mid-West

> *The production of biofuels in the USA has been a huge success for our country. By producing biofuels we have made millions of dollars for the country and created thousands of jobs. It also means we have not needed to import so many fuels, saving the country money.*

Senator

GM crops

> *GM crops are revolutionary and have completely changed the face of farming. Farmers who previously found it impossible to farm in hot, dry areas such as the Great Plains are now able to farm productively.*

Scientist for GM crops

> *As far as I'm concerned there has not been enough research into the effects of GM crops on people's health. It seems to me that altering the DNA of plants can have damaging effects on health.*

Health Minister

Activities continued...

> Every year I lose between 10% and 30% of my crops to freezing temperatures. This has been getting worse over the last ten years. I rely very heavily on GM crops because they have been designed to withstand the freezing winter temperatures and therefore I won't lose so much money.

Farmer in North Dakota

> I see the benefits to farmers of using GM crops. However, I cannot fully support their decision to use them. New types of crops that have been developed in a laboratory and are entering the food chain could pose problems not only to human health, but also to the future and safety of many wildlife species.

Scientist against GM crops

Organic farming

> I grow organic fruit and vegetables reluctantly. The only reason why I have started to farm this way is because the market demands it. I find the whole process to be hugely time consuming and there is less produced at the end, so I have to raise prices. The difficult growing conditions in Texas make the problem worse.

Organic farmer

> I'm very glad organic produce can now be purchased in the supermarket. I think that the difference between conventional and organic produce is like night and day. Organic vegetables and meat taste 100 times better than non-organic produce and there is no risk to my health.

Organic consumer

> I've not found the introduction of organic farming to benefit me personally. Consumers aren't willing to pay such high prices for goods that they can buy more cheaply elsewhere. I've started to grow some GM corn as well, as I find the growing season in Oklahoma is short and at times quite difficult, I couldn't grow GM crops if I was an organic farmer. I don't know why any farmer in the Great Plains would choose to grow organically.

Conventional farmer

> I think the whole business of organic farming and organic produce is ridiculous. For years we've been eating conventional crops and no harm has come to anyone. Why would anyone choose to pay such high prices for foods that they can buy cheaper? I certainly wouldn't pay $1 for an apple that I can get for 35 cents.

Conventional consumer

Now complete the 'I can do' boxes for this chapter.

Chapter 26

This chapter looks at farming in Kerala, India.

The rural landscape in a developing country: Kerala, India

By the end of this chapter, you should be able to:

✓ describe the location and climate of Kerala
✓ describe some features of the rural landscape here
✓ describe some characteristics of subsistent intensive farming.

Location

Kerala is a state in the south-west of India. It is flat and low near the coast but rises to over 2000 metres inland in the Western Ghats. It is a rainy region, averaging 3000 mm per year (Glasgow receives 1200 mm) but this is concentrated into just four months – the wet monsoon season, from June to September. It is hot all year, being just a few degrees north of the equator.

Although it is not the richest state, its people have the highest life expectancy in India and also the highest literacy rates. It is an important tourist region, but half the people still earn their living from farming. It has seven cities, each with over a million people but farmland takes up 54 per cent of the land and forestry 27 per cent.

26

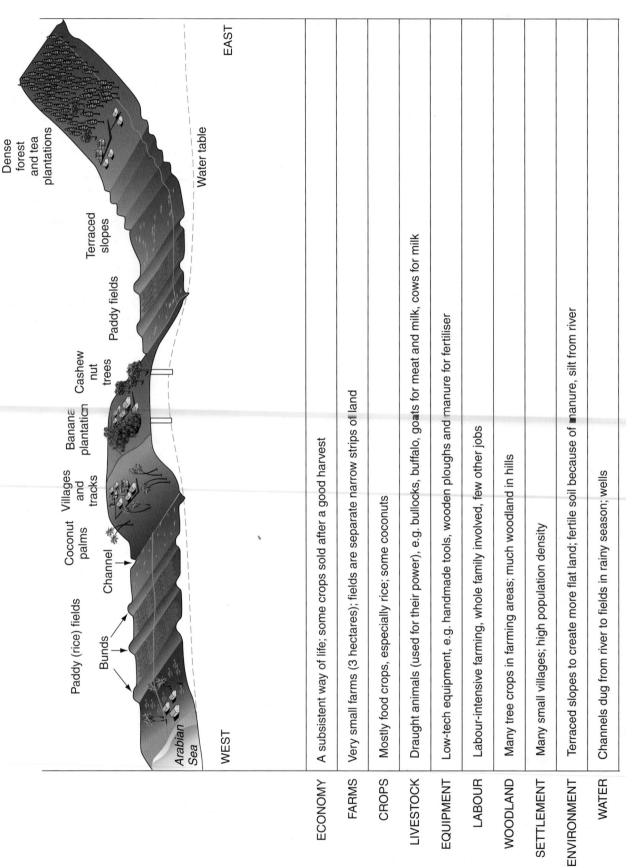

WEST

Arabian Sea

Paddy (rice) fields

Bunds

Channel

Coconut palms

Villages and tracks

Banana plantation

Cashew nut trees

Paddy fields

Terraced slopes

Dense forest and tea plantations

Water table

EAST

ECONOMY	A subsistent way of life; some crops sold after a good harvest
FARMS	Very small farms (3 hectares); fields are separate narrow strips of land
CROPS	Mostly food crops, especially rice; some coconuts
LIVESTOCK	Draught animals (used for their power), e.g. bullocks, buffalo, goats for meat and milk, cows for milk
EQUIPMENT	Low-tech equipment, e.g. handmade tools, wooden ploughs and manure for fertiliser
LABOUR	Labour-intensive farming, whole family involved, few other jobs
WOODLAND	Many tree crops in farming areas; much woodland in hills
SETTLEMENT	Many small villages; high population density
ENVIRONMENT	Terraced slopes to create more flat land; fertile soil because of manure, silt from river
WATER	Channels dug from river to fields in rainy season; wells

Figure 26.1
Typical rural landscape in Kerala

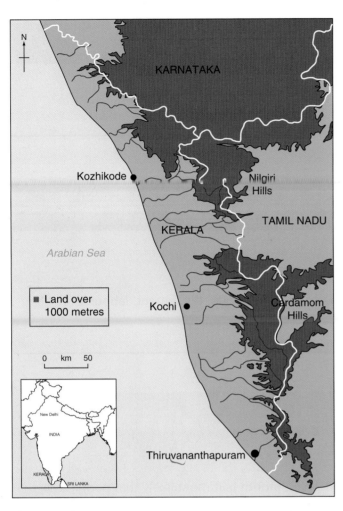

Figure 26.2
State of Kerala in India

A typical rural landscape in Kerala

Figure 26.1 shows a typical area of countryside in Kerala. It is a cross-section, showing the different land uses. Until recently, most **people were subsistence farmers**, growing food for their families only, and the **most important food crop was rice**. Farms are intensive, which means they are small, but every single hectare (2.5 acres) of rice needs 2000 hours of work each year. For example, crops have to be planted, cared for and harvested; the land has to be prepared, fertilised and weeded; bunds and terraces need to be built and repaired. This is mostly done by hand, with only low-tech, basic equipment to help. And it is done twice a year because **farmers are able to have two harvests a year. Water comes from wells** and is also diverted from rivers onto fields during the rainy season.

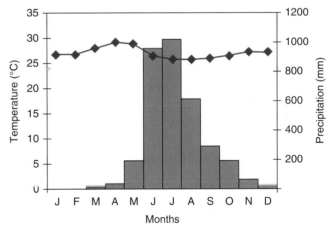

Figure 26.3
Climate of coastal Kerala

National 4

1. Where is Kerala?
2. Describe the climate in Kerala.
3. What is meant by *subsistence farming*?
4. Rice is the most important food crop but there are also tree crops. Name three.
5. Why is farming here low-tech?
6. How is the soil kept fertile?
7. Farms in Kerala are *intensive*. Explain what this means.

National 4 continued...

8. Why are the hillsides terraced?
9. Describe the main tasks on a rice farm.
10. Apart from farmland, what else makes up the rural landscape in Kerala?

National 5

1. Describe the location of Kerala within India.
2. Describe the climate of Kerala shown in Figure 26.3.
3. (a) What is meant by subsistence farming?
   (b) Explain how being subsistent affects the type of farming: crops, equipment, labour, etc.
4. Describe the benefits of terracing hillsides.
5. Describe the main land uses in rural Kerala.

Activities

Activity A

Look at the climate graph for Kerala (Figure 26.3). In which **month** is it most likely that people will:

- plant rice
- harvest rice
- put out forest fires
- be short of work
- be short of water
- collect firewood
- go hungry
- catch malaria
- go fishing?

Activity B

1. Most farmers in the UK live in the middle of their farmland; in Kerala most people live in villages. Why?
2. Farmers in the UK often have problems with poor weather, outbreaks of disease amongst their animals or crops, and low prices. Do you think farmers in Kerala are affected in a similar way?

Now complete the 'I can do' boxes for this chapter.

Chapter

27

This chapter looks at farming changes in Kerala, India.

Rural change in Kerala, India (1)

By the end of this chapter, you should be able to:

✓ describe some of the changes to the farming landscape in Kerala
✓ give examples of new technology on farms here, and the reasons for it
✓ give examples of farm diversification, and the reasons for it

Figure 27.1 shows how much the countryside in Kerala has changed in recent years. Many of the changes have taken place because of advances in technology.

New technology

Farmers now have access to better equipment, better seeds and better methods than ever before. This has improved farming in Kerala in many ways – some of these are shown in Figure 27.2.

27

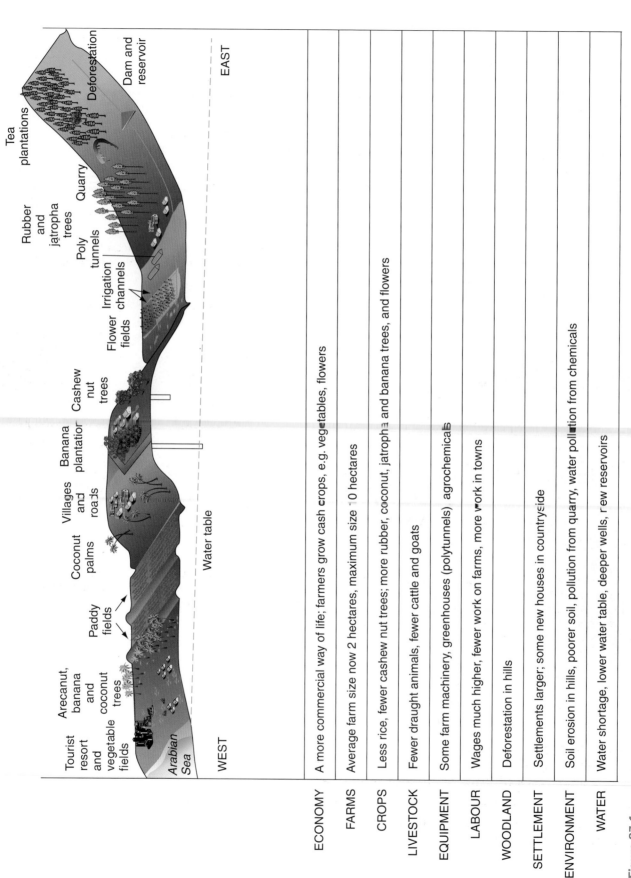

ECONOMY	A more commercial way of life; farmers grow cash crops, e.g. vegetables, flowers
FARMS	Average farm size now 2 hectares, maximum size 10 hectares
CROPS	Less rice, fewer cashew nut trees; more rubber, coconut, jatropha and banana trees, and flowers
LIVESTOCK	Fewer draught animals, fewer cattle and goats
EQUIPMENT	Some farm machinery, greenhouses (polytunnels) agrochemicals
LABOUR	Wages much higher, fewer work on farms, more work in towns
WOODLAND	Deforestation in hills
SETTLEMENT	Settlements larger; some new houses in countryside
ENVIRONMENT	Soil erosion in hills, poorer soil, pollution from quarry, water pollution from chemicals
WATER	Water shortage, lower water table, deeper wells, new reservoirs

Figure 27.1
Changes to the rural landscape in Kerala

Large-scale irrigation
–Putting dams across rivers creates reservoirs which give
  reliable water supply all year
–Farmers can now grow many crops
–Farmers can have two or three harvests per year

Greenhouses
–These are mostly polythene tunnels
–They allow the farmer to control the climate so plants can
  grow at any time
–They allow more types of plants to grow
–Farmers can have many harvests per year

Agro-chemicals
–Artificial fertilisers help crops to grow better and pesticides,
  fungicides and other chemicals kill pests and diseases
–As a result, crops produce higher yields but every year more
  and more chemicals need to be applied to make the soil
  fertile again

Biogas plants
–These have existed for many years but are improving
–They convert animal manure and human sewage into gas
  which is then used for heating and lighting in the home
–They are cheap to build

Figure 27.2
New technologies for farming

Diversification

New technology has led to changes on farms. But there have been many other
changes – see Figure 27.3. **When farmers change from the old traditional
ways to new ways of farming, it is called *diversification*.**

There have been other changes as well. There are fewer terraces now because less
rice is grown and some farmers are now experimenting with growing biofuels and
GM cotton (see Chapter 28).

Type of diversification	Reason
Commercial farming	Possibly the most useful farming development has been the increase in proper, surfaced roads throughout Kerala. This has allowed farmers to sell their produce.
More high-priced crops grown e.g. vegetables, flowers	There are (a) more hotels needing them, (b) more people in Kerala with money to buy food, (c) more greenhouses available in which to grow them.
Less rice grown	Because (a) it is too costly to grow and (b) if farmers sell it, the price is too low. Rice is costly to grow because it needs extra casual labour, and wages are much higher now. It also needs more and more chemicals to grow well. Prices are low because so much cheap rice is imported (including subsidised rice from the USA).
Less organic farming	More agrochemicals are now available and more farmers have money to buy them.

Figure 27.3
Farming changes in Kerala

National 4

1. Look at Figure 26.1 which shows the old landscape of Kerala, and at Figure 27.1 which shows today's landscape.
   Decide whether each of these statements is **true** or **false**.
   (a) Farming is more commercial now
   (b) Farm size has increased to 10 hectares.
   (c) More cash crops are grown now.
   (d) More animals are found on farms now.
   (e) There is more farm equipment used.
   (f) More people work on farms.
   (g) There are more paddy fields now.
   (h) There are more trees.
   (i) There is more water available.
2. Which of the four examples of new technology on Kerala farms listed below has been the most helpful to farmers? Give reasons for your answer.

   large-scale irrigation   greenhouses   agrochemicals   biogas plants
3. Every family in Kerala eats rice. So why is less rice grown now?
4. What effect have new hotels had on farming?
5. What effect have new roads had on farming?
6. Give two examples of farm diversification and explain why they have happened.

National 5

1. Look at Figure 26.1 which shows the old landscape of Kerala, and Figure 27.1 which shows the landscape as it is today.
   Describe the main changes to the types of farming found in Kerala.
2. Do the farmers have to spend more money now on their farms, or less? Give reasons for your answer.
3. Apart from the farms, describe some of the main changes to the rural landscape.
4. Which two of the four examples of new technology on Kerala farms listed below have been the most helpful to farmers? Give reasons for your answer.

   large-scale irrigation   greenhouses   agrochemicals   biogas plants

5. Every family in Kerala eats rice. So why is less rice grown now?
6. Explain why many farmers in Kerala now grow cash crops.

Activities

Activity A

What is the connection between the following pairs of words (in relation to Kerala)?

1. commercial farming   rice growing
2. fewer terraces   low price of rice
3. dried-up river   deep well
4. polytunnels   flowers
5. deforestation   quarry
6. roads   tourism

Activity B

Farmer X lives in a village in Kerala near a beach which until recently had no electricity. He grew a couple of hectares of rice in paddy fields. He also had a few coconut trees, four dairy cows and some goats.
Four technological developments have become available to him recently:

- Polytunnels from a new local company that makes them
- Water from a new large dam and reservoir
- An affordable biogas plant
- A wide range of agrochemicals.

Which development will be most useful to the farmer?

Now complete the 'I can do' boxes for this chapter.

Chapter 28

This chapter looks at farming changes in Kerala, India.

Rural change in Kerala, India (2)

By the end of this chapter, you should be able to:

✓ describe the advantages and disadvantages of growing biofuels in Kerala

✓ describe the arguments for and against growing GM crops in Kerala

✓ give examples of the ways in which the government affects farming here.

Biofuels

While the Great Plains of the USA has seen a big increase recently in biofuel crops, in India there has been a much smaller increase – mostly in sugarcane and jatropha. India is the world's biggest grower of sugarcane but only a tiny fraction is used to make ethanol (a type of biofuel). It could produce a lot more but growing crops to be used as biofuel is very controversial. The state of Kerala grows a little sugarcane but it grows more jatropha for biofuel.

The problems with using sugarcane as biofuel

Sugarcane takes up land that could be used for growing food. About one-quarter of the people in India do not have enough food to eat. It is difficult for farmers to justify growing 'food for cars' instead of 'food for people'.

- If more land is used for sugarcane, **there is less food grown**. If less food (such as rice or wheat) is grown, the price rises. Then, poorer people cannot afford it and go hungry.

- Sugarcane uses a lot of water and for many months of the year India gets very little rain. **Growing sugarcane makes the water shortage worse**.
- In some places **trees have been cut down to make land for growing sugar**, but deforestation causes many problems. It leads to increased flooding, more greenhouse gases in the atmosphere and the soil can be easily eroded, often being washed down the hillside by heavy rains. This can make the land useless for farming.
- Also in India there are **too few sugar refineries** making biofuel and the cost of producing it is higher than the price farmers can get for it.

Benefits of growing crops for biofuel

Figure 28.1

- **It reduces the amount and cost of oil that India has to import**. It currently imports 70 per cent of all the oil it needs, which is very expensive.
- The demand for oil in India is growing rapidly each year as more factories are built and more people own cars.
- **Using biofuels should lower the cost of fuel**, which should help reduce the cost of transport. This should in turn help industries, so factories can employ more people who will then have a higher standard of living.
- Burning biofuels puts fewer greenhouse gases into the atmosphere than does the burning of fossil fuels such as petroleum and coal. Using biofuels should reduce global warming.

Benefits of growing jatropha for biofuel

A few years ago scientists discovered the benefits of growing **the jatropha plant**. Its seeds can be crushed to produce oil that can be used as biofuel. In addition, it does not have the same growing disadvantages as sugarcane.

Figure 28.2

- It **grows in poor soil**, so it can be grown on land not suitable for growing food.
- It is **labour-intensive** work, so many workers need to be employed – and paid.
- It does not need to be processed in a large factory – it **can be used locally** in diesel generators, irrigation pumps and farm machinery. In this way it will help each community become more mechanised and have more electricity.

Problems with growing the jatropha plant for biofuel

Figure 28.3

- **Farmers have had mixed results after growing jatropha**. Some find that it does not grow well on poor soil, so less oil is produced.
- Some farmers say that **it uses a lot of water**.

- Because they are producing less oil than expected, farmers have to sell it at a high price, which is higher than the diesel oil that people can buy. So they find it difficult to sell.

Government influence

The government influences farmers more than ever before. It encourages farmers to grow biofuels. **It provides price support to farmers growing sugarcane and jatropha**, which means the farmers are offered a higher price. It gives grants to farmers to start growing jatropha.

The government of Kerala also **gives grants for greenhouses** on farms. It gives a lot of farming advice and there are even **programmes on television that give farming information**.

In contrast, the national government has **banned the growing of GM crops**. This is also highly controversial.

Figure 28.4

Genetically modified crops

GM crops are crops whose genes have been altered. This is done in a science laboratory. Plants are then grown on special experimental farms to find out whether they can grow successfully outside. The growing of genetically modified crops in India is currently banned, but there are frequent arguments about this decision – see Figure 28.5.

Figure 28.5

National 4

1. What are the main advantages for India of growing biofuels?
2. *less food grown   higher food prices   water shortages   deforestation*
   These are the main problems of growing sugarcane as a biofuel. Which of these is the most serious problem in India, do you think? Give reasons for your answer.
3. Jatropha is another biofuel crop which grows in poor soil. Why is it so useful?
4. Look at Figure 28.5 which shows people discussing GM crops in India.
   Draw a table with two columns: **Advantages to India** and **Disadvantages to India**.
   Write each person's comments in the correct column.
5. (a) *GM crops will allow us to grow more food.*
      Explain why this is a big advantage to India.
   (b) *GM crops need fewer chemicals to grow.*
      Explain why this is an advantage to India.
6. Describe two ways in which the government affects farming in Kerala.

National 5

1. Describe convincingly the two main advantages to India of growing biofuels.
2. Explain why growing jatropha might be better in India than growing sugarcane as a biofuel.
3. Describe the two main reasons why both sugarcane and jatropha are still not grown very much in India.
4. Explain fully the advantages of growing GM crops in India.
5. (a) Why do you think the Indian government banned GM crops?
   (b) In what other ways does the government affect farming?

Activities

Activity A

Design an eye-catching poster persuading the Indian government to allow GM crops to be grown in India.

Activity B

Figure 28.5 shows a discussion about GM crops. Make up another discussion between several people about growing biofuels in India. Try to include as many arguments as possible.

Now complete the 'I can do' boxes for this chapter.

'I can do' self-assessment checklist

	Red	Yellow	Green	Comment
Chapter 1 World population distribution				
Give examples of countries with a high population density				
Give examples of countries with a low population density				
Describe some of the reasons for the world's population distribution				
Chapter 2 Urban and rural population				
Describe the differences in urban and rural populations in developed and developing countries				
Give reasons for these differences				
Describe megacities and give examples				
Chapter 3 Population change				
Describe what is meant by birth rate, death rate and natural increase				
Outline the difference in birth rates and death rates between developing and developed countries				
Give reasons for these differences				
Chapter 4 The effects of rapid population growth				
Describe birth and death rates in countries with rapidly growing populations				
Describe the problems associated with countries with a rapid population growth				
Describe the benefits for countries with a rapid population growth				
Chapter 5 The effects of slow population growth				
Describe birth and death rates in countries with slowly growing populations				
Describe the problems for countries with slowly growing populations				
Describe the benefits for countries with slowly growing populations				

Chapter 6 The Demographic Transition Model				
Describe how the population changes at each stage of the Demographic Transition Model				
Explain why birth rates and death rates change at each stage				
Give examples of countries that fit into each stage				
Chapter 7 Measuring development (1)				
Provide a definition for development				
Give examples of economic indicators of development				
Describe social indicators of development				
Chapter 8 Measuring development (2)				
Give reasons why combined indicators of development are more reliable than single indicators				
Describe the Physical Quality of Life Index				
Describe the Human Development Index				
Chapter 9 Reasons for differences in development levels (1)				
List some differences between developed and developing countries				
List some of the physical factors affecting development				
Explain how physical factors affect development				
Chapter 10 Reasons for differences in development levels (2)				
Describe the impact of population growth on development				
Explain the connection between industrialisation and development				
Give reasons why trade has an impact on development.				
Chapter 11 Land uses in developed world cities				
Understand why cities grow				
List the main land uses in a developed city				
Understand one land use model of a developed city				

Chapter 12 Land use zones in developed world cities				
List the four main land use zones in a developed city				
List several characteristics of each zone				
Understand some of the reasons for those characteristics				
Chapter 13 Case study of a developed city: Glasgow, Scotland				
Know how Glasgow's population has changed over time				
Understand some of the reasons why Glasgow has grown				
Understand how Glasgow's land use zones developed				
Chapter 14 Changes in Glasgow's CBD				
Understand the reasons for traffic congestion in Glasgow's CBD				
Describe several effects of and solutions to traffic congestion here				
Describe and explain some of the main shopping changes				
Chapter 15 Changes in Glasgow's inner city (1)				
Describe the problems in The Gorbals area of Glasgow in the 1950s				
Describe some recent changes in The Gorbals				
Describe how these changes have improved The Gorbals				
Chapter 16 Changes in Glasgow's inner city (2)				
Describe the problems in the Old Docks area of Glasgow in the 1960s				
Describe some recent changes in the Old Docks				
Describe how these changes have improved the Old Docks				
Chapter 17 Changes in Glasgow's suburbs				
List some of the features of the Greenlaw development in Glasgow's suburbs				
Explain why people want to move to Glasgow's suburbs				
Explain why industry and shops want to move to Glasgow's suburbs				

Chapter 18 Conflicts in Glasgow's suburbs			
Understand what is meant by urban sprawl			
Describe some good and bad effects of urban sprawl in Glasgow			
Describe some solutions to urban sprawl in Glasgow			
Chapter 19 Case study of a developing city: Mumbai, India			
Describe the site of Mumbai			
Describe how Mumbai has grown over time			
Give some of the reasons why it has grown			
Chapter 20 Housing problems in Mumbai			
Describe some features of squatter camps and shanty towns			
Describe some of their problems			
Give examples of solutions to the housing problems in Mumbai			
Chapter 21 Case study of a shanty town in Mumbai: Dharavi (1)			
Describe the growth of Dharavi			
Describe some of the features of Dharavi			
Describe some of the problems of Dharavi			
Chapter 22 Case study of a shanty town in Mumbai: Dharavi (2)			
Describe some of the benefits of Dharavi			
Describe some features of the Dharavi Redevelopment Project			
Describe some features of a self-improvement plan for Dharavi			
Chapter 23 The rural landscape in a developed country: the Great Plains, USA			
Describe the location and physical landscape of the Great Plains			
Describe the land use pattern in the Great Plains			
Describe the main characteristics of extensive commercial farming here			

Chapter 24 Rural change in the Great Plains, USA (1)				
Describe some of the new technology and methods used on farms in the Great Plains				
Give examples of how farms here have diversified				
Give examples of how the government affects farming here				
Chapter 25 Rural change in the Great Plains, USA (2)				
Describe the reasons for and against growing biofuels in the Great Plains				
Give reasons to support and oppose the use of genetically modified crops				
Describe some of the reasons why farmers grow organic produce				
Chapter 26 The rural landscape in a developing country: Kerala, India				
Describe the location and climate of Kerala				
Describe some features of the rural landscape here				
Describe some characteristics of subsistent intensive farming				
Chapter 27 Rural change in Kerala, India (1)				
Describe some of the changes to the farming landscape in Kerala				
Give examples of new technology on farms here, and the reasons for it				
Give examples of farm diversification, and the reasons for it				
Chapter 28 Rural change in Kerala, India (2)				
Describe the advantages and disadvantages of growing biofuels in Kerala				
Describe the arguments for and against growing GM crops in Kerala				
Give examples of the ways in which the government affects farming here				

Index